ONE W[...]

Polly West had met and married Piran St Just while on holiday in Paris—a thoroughly romantic situation, one might have thought. Except that the marriage itself was anything but romantic—a mere business arrangement made for the sake of Piran's little nephew Jules. Would the thought that she had secured the child's happiness compensate Polly for the fact that her husband would never love her?

Books you will enjoy
by MARJORIE LEWTY

MAKESHIFT MARRIAGE

Blake Morden relied on his secretary Maggie Webster for everything—except the one thing she wanted him to rely on her for. He would never love her, as she had loved him for so long. But then his fiancée jilted him and, on the rebound, he asked Maggie to marry him ...

A GIRL BEWITCHED

Emma's young cousin Lisa seemed to have been absolutely bewitched by Trent Marston, and heartbroken when he callously walked out on her. Now that Lisa had married, presumably on the rebound, that would be the end of Trent, Emma thought—only to find she was in danger of becoming bewitched by him herself!

BEYOND THE LAGOON

'God preserve me from rich men's daughters,' said Gideon North contemptuously. Susan French wasn't rich at all—but she was pretending to be Della Benton, who was, so if and when Gideon discovered the deception, it was hardly going to improve his opinion of her, was it? And why did she care so much?

ONE WHO KISSES

BY

MARJORIE LEWTY

MILLS & BOON LIMITED
15–16 BROOK'S MEWS
LONDON W1A 1DR

First published 1983
Australian copyright 1983
Philippine copyright 1983
This edition 1983

© Marjorie Lewty 1983

ISBN 0 263 74203 2

Set in Monophoto Plantin 10 on 11pt
01—0483 - 56514

Made and printed in Great Britain by
Richard Clay (The Chaucer Press) Ltd,
Bungay, Suffolk

CHAPTER ONE

PARIS in September. It was so beautiful that it almost made up for all the disappointments of the last few weeks, Polly told herself, stepping out briskly along the wide, tree-lined boulevard.

It had rained in the night and the morning air had a clean, washed smell. The trees rustled their laundered greenery in the breeze. On the pavements outside the cafés the little tables would soon be filled with people, chatting and drinking coffee under the striped canopies while they lazily watched the world go by, but this early in the morning the tables were empty, waiting.

Polly stopped and consulted her map of Paris, on which she had put a cross against the coach station she was making for. This was the last day of her five-day holiday and she had saved the greatest treat until the end—a day trip to see Chartres Cathedral.

She turned off the boulevard and crossed the gardens, taking a short cut over the grass. Two French boys in black berets—students probably—strolled towards her, deliberately changing direction as they drew near. They smiled cheekily as they reached her, their dark, laughing eyes resting in blatant appreciation on the slender figure in tight jeans and frilly white blouse, the silky wheat-fair hair, the piquante face with its tilted little nose and pretty mouth.

The morning air was so exhilarating that Polly very nearly smiled back, but remembered in time that it was unwise to smile at strange men in a foreign country. So she walked on, chin held high, ignoring the remarks they called after her. Perhaps fortunately her knowledge of the French language wasn't up to translating them.

This was the penalty of coming abroad on her own. But being on her own was the way she wanted it. She could have been out with that rather nice American boy who was staying at her hotel with his parents. But she wasn't looking for romance on her Paris holiday, not so soon after Mike.

Her face clouded as she thought of Mike, far away up in Lancaster, starting out on his first teaching job. If only her own appointment hadn't fallen through at the last minute she would have been up there with him now, teaching at the same school, deepening the friendship they had struck up in college, only a couple of days before the end of their final term.

It had seemed to Polly like the beginning of something wonderful when Mike Tarrent, tall and blond and athletic, and every girl student's pin-up, had singled her out at the graduation dance. When they discovered that they both had appointments to start in September at the same school in Lancaster it seemed like Fate.

And then, the next day, the awful news came through that the teacher whom Polly had been appointed to replace temporarily had recovered unexpectedly from her illness and would be able to resume her job again at the beginning of the new term in September.

Polly was devastated, and Mike had comforted her. 'Never mind, Poll, you can still come up to Lancaster with me. The flat I've got booked is big enough for the two of us and you can probably pick up a job. How about supply teaching?'

'Share your flat?' Polly's blue eyes opened very wide. 'Do you mean——?'

'Why not?' Mike grinned. 'Seems a good idea to me.'

'But we haven't—I mean, we hardly know each other——'

He bent his blond head and nuzzled her ear. 'There's one excellent way of getting over that small difficulty, my sweet. Never been known to fail. Shall I expound further?'

'No, thanks, I can imagine.' She pulled a face at him. Better to take this as lightly as he seemed to be doing. 'Thanks for the offer, Mike, but the answer's no.'

He had argued a bit, pleaded a bit, but she knew he wasn't heartbroken. There would be lots of pretty girls in Lancaster. She wasn't heartbroken either, she assured herself for the hundredth time now, her sandals sinking into the soft turf as she quickened her pace. But Mike was fun, he was a marvellous companion and she was dreadfully disappointed that she would probably never see him again. It was better this way, she tried to believe. If she had agreed to go with him she would have fallen in love with him, and that wouldn't have been a good idea. He was obviously not the kind of young man with marriage on his mind, and Polly knew she wasn't the kind of girl who could take an affair lightly and let it go with a smile and a wave when it was over.

So—better not. Yes, she was glad she had refused and she mustn't let herself get depressed because she was alone in Paris, this city of romance. She had chosen to give herself this short holiday, using up at least half of her savings from her holiday job as a temporary waitress in Bournemouth, to take her mind off her disappointment. It was a very sensible thing to do, surely, and she had enjoyed it all tremendously. She would buy a picture postcard in Chartres to send to Mike, just so that he wouldn't forget her altogether. And perhaps, she thought as she turned out of the park, if it was meant to happen, they would meet again one day.

Ah, here was the coach station, just as they had told her at the hotel. Two shiny blue coaches were pulled up under the trees on the opposite side of the road. One had *Fontainebleau* on the indicator and the other *Chartres*. Polly hurried across the road. The driver of her coach was leaning against the mudguard of his vehicle, smoking the usual Gauloise. She showed him her booking ticket and he jerked his head sideways and upwards.

She climbed into the coach. It was nearly full and she was met by a buzz of American and German and other languages she didn't recognise. There was one vacant double seat near the front and she slid thankfully into the inside seat. Lucky to be beside the window; from here she could survey the passing scene in comfort. So far, in her five-day holiday, she hadn't been outside Paris itself. This drive to Chartres would give her some idea of the countryside, as well as a sight of what was, perhaps, the most beautiful cathedral ever to have been built.

A thin woman in a red dress splashily patterned with roses climbed aboard. She had a sharp face and elaborately-dressed black hair and she was pulling a small boy of about six behind her, dragging him up the steep step into the coach without much consideration for his short legs—which looked to Polly much too spindly for a boy of that age.

The woman stood looking round the inside of the coach with darting, beady eyes and Polly was aware that she herself had just taken the only double seat left. The little boy looked scared and he clung to the woman's hand. 'Where can I sit,

Grand'maman?' he quavered in French.

She pushed him into a seat at the front of the coach and sat down herself next to Polly. 'Be quiet now, Jules,' she snapped. 'You can watch the driver from there. *Tais-toi!*' she added sharply, as he began to whimper, and he looked at her with large, frightened eyes and obeyed.

Polly's heart went out to the child. She said in her careful French, 'Shall I move, so that the little boy can sit beside you, *madame*?'

The woman shook her head. '*Non, celà ne fait rien. He has to learn, n'est-ce pas?*' The sharp nose twitched and Madame smoothed her skirt over her knees. 'He will ask me questions all the time if he sits beside me. He is a little nuisance with his questions.'

Polly was of the opinion that it was a healthy thing for a child to ask questions, but she didn't argue the point. Instead she smiled faintly and turned her head to look out of the window.

A long, grey, expensive-looking car was pulling up on the opposite side of the road. A man got out and stood looking around. Then he crossed the road purposefully towards the Chartres coach and stopped just below where Polly was sitting, dark eyes raking the passengers inside.

She watched him with interest. Indeed, it would have been difficult not to feel interest, for he was the most immediately impressive man she had ever seen. With his dark hair and eyes he might have been French, but not many Frenchmen were that tall or had that springiness in their hair. English, she thought. Scottish perhaps, or even American. Most probably English. He had the almost insolent quiet self-possession she had noticed in many of the English during her stay at the hotel. She had noticed, too, that the French were definitely *not* impressed. The

English, they seemed to infer, with their cynical shrug, *trop sur de soi!* Too cocky, in fact!

The dark eyes stopped their roving and came to rest, and Polly's heart gave a sudden strange leap, for he seemed to be staring straight at her. Then she relaxed as she realised that her neighbour in the red dress was the object of his hard scrutiny.

The woman muttered something under her breath and turned away, but the man had recognized her and had one foot, now, on the step of the coach. The driver roused himself sufficiently to make a gesture of protest and an exchange of words followed, during which the tall man remained impassive while the driver waved his arms about a good deal. Finally something changed hands, the driver lit another cigarette and the man swung himself easily up into the coach and stood towering over the woman in the red dress. Polly couldn't resist stealing a glance at him. Close to, he looked even more formidable. He was dressed casually in cords and a checked shirt, the sleeves rolled up to show powerful bronzed forearms. His shoulders were wide and muscular and there was a dark shadow on his chin. A very tough customer indeed, thought Polly, looking away quickly.

'Good morning, *madame.*' He spoke in French, but Polly was sure now that he was English. His voice was deep and cultured, contrasting oddly with the roughness of his appearance.

The woman's eyes avoided his. 'What do you want?' she said sullenly, antagonism oozing from every pore.

'I think you know what I want, *madame.* May I trouble you to come outside and speak to me briefly about the matter?'

For a moment Polly thought the woman was going to refuse. She foresaw trouble. This wasn't a man to be refused anything. But, with a muttered word, her

neighbour pulled herself up out of her seat, the red
dress clinging tightly to her, and followed the man out
of the coach. As he passed the small boy in the front
seat he paused for a second, resting a hand lightly on
the smooth, dark head. The boy looked up, startled,
but with no sign of recognition, and then the man had
passed him and jumped down to the pavement. He
held out his hand politely to assist the woman, but
she ignored it and took her time to climb down the
step, her every movement indicating in no uncertain
manner that she was being put to great inconvenience.

For perhaps five minutes the two of them stood
arguing beneath the trees, and Polly watched them,
fascinated. Their voices didn't reach her through the
window, but in dumb show it was obvious that some
very unpleasant words were being exchanged. The
Frenchwoman's face was distorted with anger. Her
hands moved in jerky, furious gestures as if she would
like to attack the man physically. He, on the other
hand, remained apparently calm. Only the harsh twist
of his mouth and the contempt in his dark, hooded
eyes betrayed his emotion.

What a shocker, thought Polly, half amused and yet
oddly unnerved by the sight of that grim, inflexible
face. It had nothing to do with her, of course, but she
wouldn't like to be on the receiving end of that man's
disapproval. She realised that she was staring at the
two of them and looked away quickly.

A moment or two later the woman came back into
the coach. The driver squeezed out his cigarette and
climbed in behind the wheel. The doors swished
to, the engine spluttered into life and they were
away.

The last thing Polly saw was the tall, somehow
menacing figure of the dark man, standing staring
grimly after the coach. She chuckled to herself. It was

rather fun to make a drama out of what was no doubt a run-of-the-mill family feud. Or perhaps the woman in the red dress owed him money—or perhaps——

Her flight of imagination came to an abrupt end as she heard a strangled sigh and saw that her neighbour was shaking all over, her face putty-coloured.

Polly put a hand on her arm. 'Are you feeling ill? Shall I tell the driver to stop?'

'*Non, non.*' The beady eyes stared straight ahead. 'In a moment I shall recover.' She lay back, closing her eyes.

The boy had climbed up in his seat and was peering over the top. 'Grand'maman, Grand'maman, who was the man? What is the matter?'

The woman appeared not to hear. Polly leaned forward, a finger to her lips. 'Ssh, Jules,' she said, very low. 'Your grandmother is not feeling well, but she will soon be better.' She wished she were more fluent in French. He looked so pale and anxious and she would have liked to be able to console him.

He stared at her for a moment, as if summing up this stranger who spoke to him. His dark eyes were enormous in his small, pale face, the lids lowered slightly. With a slight shock Polly saw a strong resemblance to the man who had caused all the trouble. Evidently it *had* been a family quarrel.

The boy glanced at his grandmother and then back at Polly. 'Are you English?' he said.

A bilingual child—that was a relief. Polly smiled at him. 'Yes, I'm English. And you're French, aren't you?'

'Only half,' he said. 'My daddy was English and my *maman* is French.' His lower lip drooped and he looked as if he might cry.

Polly said quickly, 'Look at those funny houses over there, Jules.'

He looked. 'Those aren't houses, it's a windmill, silly!'

She pretended to peer out of the window. 'Of course it is, how stupid of me. Do you know about windmills, Jules?'

'I know about all sorts of buildings,' he said in a superior tone. 'I am going to be an architect, you see. My daddy was an artist,' he volunteered confidentially.

No father, evidently, poor mite. Polly wondered where his mother was and why he was in the care of his grandmother who quite patently wasn't interested in him.

'Can I come and sit by you?' He sounded eager now. 'I could tell you about the cathedral. It has flying butt-resses,' he added carefully. 'They help to prop it up in case it falls down.'

'Really? Now I didn't know that.' Polly resisted her impulse to smile.

'Yes.' Jules nodded importantly. 'And it's been burned down lots and lots of times, but they built it up again. My father told me all about it when I was little. He was going to take me to see it, only he died.' He spoke so matter-of-factly that Polly guessed that his father's death couldn't have been very recent. 'So I made Grand'maman bring me.' Jules went on. 'I've asked her and asked her, but she never would.' He glanced briefly at the woman beside Polly. Her eyes were still closed, but her face had lost its papery whiteness and resumed its normal sallow colour under its heavy make-up. 'But today she said we could come. She said it would get me out of the way.'

Get him out of the way? Of what? Polly wondered. Or—more likely—of whom? A dark, arrogant figure suddenly appeared before her mind's eye.

'Can I come and sit by you?' the boy asked again.

His grandmother opened her eyes suddenly. 'Jules!' she hissed. 'Sit down and behave yourself. *Tais-toi!*'

She raised a hand threateningly and Jules slithered back into his seat.

The woman turned to Polly. 'He gets too excited,' she muttered in half-apology.

'Are you feeling better now?' Polly enquired politely.

The woman's mouth closed like a trap, and then, as if she had to release the emotion seething inside her, she began to talk. 'That man!' she began viciously. 'He is a monster, a——' There followed several words that Polly could only guess at, but the general tone was as offensive as the woman could make it. She almost spat the words out. 'He is Jules' uncle, you know, and now that the boy's mother—my dear daughter—can no longer look after him, that man wants to take him away from me, back to England. But I will not allow it. I will fight him with every breath in my body——' She lay back in her seat, panting.

Polly didn't want to snub the woman, who was obviously in a state of extreme agitation, neither did she want to have a long story of family quarrels thrust upon her. She turned her head and looked out of the window, hoping that the woman would quieten down.

But it was not to be. The querulous voice reached her above the rumble of the coach and the hum of talk from the other passengers. 'Ninette should never have married him. I told her so, I tried to stop her, but she was only eighteen and she thought this English artist was a kind of prince. Prince—pah!' She drew her thin lips together contemptuously. 'Oh, Maurice was a nice boy, but he was under the thumb of that brother of his—the one you saw. He tried to stop the marriage, he said Maurice was too young. And when he failed he cut Maurice's allowance. He was in charge of the money, that one, and he was *mean*.' She bit out another offensive word. '*Ma pauvre petite* Ninette—to have her marriage ruined by that terrible man!'

Once started the woman seemed unable to stop. The words poured out so quickly that Polly could only get a hazy impression of the story. But by now, in spite of herself, she was interested—mostly because of the little boy Jules, who now sat quietly in the seat in front, staring out through the windscreen as the coach buzzed steadily along the wide, busy road. Poor little boy, she thought, his father killed in a car accident when the child was only three. His mother, the young Ninette, delicate and forced to go out to work to support him. The story became like a Victorian melodrama, as the wicked uncle appeared now and again, trying to take the boy from his mother, and his grandmother who, it appeared, had practically brought him up, while his mother went out to work to earn their daily bread.

'And now my poor girl is no longer able to support us this man wishes to stop the allowance altogether and take Jules away. *Quel inhumanité!*' Angry tears squeezed themselves from her beady eyes and ran down her cheeks, the mascara ploughing a dark streak through the heavy pinkish make-up.

Polly began to feel sorry for her. She wasn't exactly an engaging personality, but it seemed she had had a very poor deal. Her son-in-law dead, her daughter harassed by this terrible, inhuman man who was forcing her to give up her child.

The story continued as the coach ate up the miles towards its destination. It was just as well, Polly thought, that the passing countryside wasn't particularly interesting. Huge fields, so much vaster than English fields, with here and there a cluster of farm buildings, the tall houses looking so strange out in the countryside.

Suddenly Jules could contain himself no longer. 'Look—look there!' he squealed. 'There it is, over there,' pointing through the window into the distance, where the two mighty spires of Chartres Cathedral soared up into the blue sky.

'We're almost there, isn't that exciting?' Polly smiled at him as he twisted round in his seat.

His grandmother sniffed and took a handkerchief from her voluminous handbag, dabbing her eyes and sighing a good deal. The passengers began to gather their satchels and jackets together and get out their cameras. The coach passed into the small town and pulled up in the shadow of the cathedral itself and the tourists began to pile out. Polly, hemmed in on the inside seat, waited for the woman in the red dress to leave. She would, she planned, hang back until she could see her way to shake off her garrulous neighbour, and hope that young Jules would manage to see what he wanted of the great building that towered majestically above them.

At last the woman moved, took the boy's hand and they climbed down from the coach. Polly lingered until all the other passengers had left and then joined on at the end.

But as she stepped down she felt a small, moist hand creep into hers and there was Jules, looking up pleadingly at her.

His grandmother was scolding: '*Non, non,* Jules, you cannot go trailing round the cathedral. It is too much for my legs, walking, walking. I cannot tolerate it. We shall go to that café across the road and you may have *limonade* and I shall rest myself. It is too hot to walk.' She took out a handkerchief and dabbed her forehead.

'Oh, Grand'maman, please——' Jules's lower lip trembled and the hand that held Polly's gripped harder. 'I want to see inside. Oh, please let me go!'

'*Non*, I told you—now stop whining.' She glanced at Polly. 'He is so naughty, he tires me out.'

Polly swallowed the reply she would like to have made. 'I am going into the cathedral myself, *madame*. Would you allow Jules to come with me?'

Madame jumped at it. The prospect of an undisturbed sit-down with coffee and cakes was too tempting to resist. She could even afford Jules a pat on the head. 'Go along then, Jules, and mind you behave yourself and say thank you to Mademoiselle.' To Polly she said, 'It is kind of you. I shall be in the café over there if you will bring Jules back to me.' She crossed the road, busy with cars and coaches, without any sign of the fatigue she was complaining of, and disappeared into the café.

Polly and Jules stood hand in hand gazing up at the overwhelming west front of the cathedral. History was Polly's subject and she had read all about the great Gothic cathedrals of France, but the actuality was beyond belief. The sheer height and magnificence of the great building; the sculptured saints, standing elongated in their rows in every portal, staring out with their blind stone eyes; the incredible complexity of the carving and tracery that covered every inch of the portals—it was awe-inspiring, and Polly, who had meant to tell Jules something of what she had learned, found herself at a loss for words.

Oddly enough, Jules didn't ask any questions. He, too, seemed struck dumb by the magnificence of the great building that soared up and up above their heads into the blue sky.

Then he shook her hand gently. 'Mademoiselle!'

'Yes?' She leaned down to him.

'They built the spires so that they could reach up to heaven, didn't they?'

'Yes, Jules, I believe they did.'

A wide grin broke over his thin face, making him look more like a normal little boy. 'I *told* Grand'maman that,' he said triumphantly, 'but she said I wasn't to make up silly stories.'

Polly fumed inwardly. She thought it insufferable to put a child down like that. She said, 'Would you like to go inside now, Jules?'

They walked up the steps and through the opening in the massive central doorway.

After the brightness of the sunlight outside, entering the interior was like walking into a black cavern. Polly drew in a breath, almost with shock, and she felt Jules's hand grip her own more tightly. The gloom and the chill and the echo of footsteps through the vast building was eerie.

'It's dark,' Jules whispered, shivering. 'Why don't they put the lights on?'

'I expect they will soon,' Polly reassured him. 'But it's easier to see the colours of the stained glass windows when the sun is shining through from the outside. Shall we walk round a bit?'

Polly could have spent hours exploring the inside of the cathedral, where each window illustrated in detail some Bible story, or some event or social scene of the period. It was gloomy, certainly, but the light pouring in through the glass threw rich vibrant patterns of blue and crimson and purple and gold on to the massive walls and pillars.

But Jules hadn't got over his fear of the dark. 'Shall we go outside again, *mademoiselle*?' He moved closer to Polly. 'And see the flying but-tresses?'

'Yes, let's,' Polly agreed amiably. She could come inside again when she had delivered Jules to his grandmother.

Back in the sunshine Jules cheered up and as they wandered slowly round the outer walls of the cathedral he pointed out various aspects of the architecture. It was amusing and rather touching to hear such a small boy talking so learnedly about octagonal towers, and facets, and gables. In some ways he seemed much older than the six years and a half that Madame had mentioned to Polly; in other ways he was a baby still, shrinking from the unknown. She got the impression of a solitary child, brought up among books rather than people.

At last she said, 'I think we ought to be going back now, Jules. Your grandmother will be wondering where we are.'

His mouth drooped. 'Oh, must we? I like being with you, *mademoiselle*,' he added shyly.

'And I like being with you, Jules,' Polly smiled. 'But I think we should go.'

He followed her obediently back to the west side, where they had parted from Madame. The traffic had thickened and cars tangled and hooted, trying to find parking places. 'Look, there she is, said Polly, and waved as she spotted the familiar red dress with its decoration of roses. Madame was standing outside the café on the opposite side of the street, looking around with nervous, jerky movements of her head.

She's worried about Jules, Polly thought; wondering where he's got to and if she was right to trust him with me. His mother had probably left him in her charge while she went out to work, and Madame must feel responsible for his safety.

Polly felt a twinge of sympathy again for the woman. She must have had an anxious time, and her daughter too, with that awful man hounding them both. What did he think he could gain? He must surely know that he wouldn't be allowed to take the boy away from his mother?

'Come along, Jules, your grandmother is over the road, waiting for us.' She held Jules's hand tightly, looking carefully at the traffic before venturing into the road.

Then it happened. She heard the scream of brakes, a dull thud, another and another as cars rammed into each other from the back. Then pandemonium broke out as people began to run into the street. Some premonition made Polly follow, still clutching Jules. She couldn't see Madame through the mass of people. She would be there among the crowd somewhere—she must be. But Polly had to be sure. She elbowed her way to the front, heard an American voice call out loudly, 'I'm a doctor. Someone get the police—an ambulance—quickly!'

A man pushed his way out of the crowd and the doctor went down on his knees beside a still figure that lay crumpled in the road, one leg stuck out at a shockingly crooked angle. There was blood on the road, the same colour as the rose-flowered red dress. The frizzy dark hair was hanging in dishevelled strands across the pallid face, where a long gash from temple to chin was starting to ooze horribly.

For a moment Polly felt desperately sick. Then Jules tugged at her arm. He was half-smothered in the crowd, he could see nothing of what lay there in the road. 'What's the matter, *mademoiselle*? Is somebody hurt?'

Polly drew in a deep breath. It was no good trying to deceive him, he would have to know soon. 'Jules, I'm afraid your grandmother has been injured,' she said, leaning down to him, pulling his small body against her. 'Don't be frightened, I'll look after you. There's a doctor here with her and they are sending for an ambulance to take her to hospital.'

Jules didn't reply directly. He stared up at her and his dark eyes met hers with a curiously unchildlike expression. 'You will stay with me, won't you, *mademoiselle*? Promise!'

'I promise,' said Polly gravely.

The boy nodded as if satisfied, and said no more.

After that everything was confusion. Police all around, shouting commands, clearing the crowd back, asking questions, writing in their notebooks. Polly was grateful for the help of the American doctor. His French was fluent—much better than hers—and when she had explained the situation to him he was able to explain it to the police. He drove Polly and Jules to the hospital himself, following the ambulance. 'This is my address in Paris,' he told Polly as he left them. 'I shall be there for a few days longer, and if there's any further way I can help, do contact me. I've explained things to the Sister-in-Charge, so I'm afraid all you can do now is to wait until they contact you and give you news of Madame's condition.' He smiled and shook Polly's hand and patted Jules's head. 'Good luck,' he said.

After that it was just waiting and waiting, in a small room with a table in the middle and chairs arranged round the walls. After a time a nurse brought Polly a cup of coffee and a fruit drink for Jules. No, she couldn't give them any news yet.

When Jules had finished his drink he laid his head against Polly and dropped off to sleep. She eased her arm round him, holding his thin little body tightly, feeling curiously protective. At the children's home where she had spent most of her life up to now, she could always be relied on to look after the little ones. She loved children—that was why she had wanted to teach.

She dropped a kiss on Jules's dark hair. He was a serious, unusual little boy, and for some reason he seemed to trust her. She vowed to herself that she would see him all right, although just how she was going to do it she couldn't, at this moment, imagine.

A long time later a doctor came in, an elderly man with grey hair and a kindly expression. Madame Brunet, he told Polly, was still in the operating theatre. It would be some considerable time before they could give any information about her condition. 'I would suggest,' he said, 'that you should take the boy home. I understand from my colleague who came with you that you are willing to look after him, *n'est-ce pas?* You understand that if you do not wish to do so the police will take care of him.'

'Oh no,' Polly said quickly. 'He is used to me, I wouldn't like to leave him with strangers.'

The doctor nodded understandingly. '*Bon. Bon.* It is good of you, *mademoiselle*. We have the address here, it was found in Madame's handbag.' He handed Polly a slip of paper. 'Also the key of the apartment. You can find your way back to Paris, yes? Your best way is to go by train, there is a good service. Do you think you can manage?'

'Oh yes, I'm sure I can,' Polly said eagerly. 'I hope Jules's mother will be at home when we get there. She won't know what has happened.'

'I hope so too,' the doctor told her. 'We tried to contact Madame's address by telephone, but with no success.' He looked down at the small boy, sleeping trustingly in Polly's arms and smiled. 'Get him home to bed as soon as you can, *mademoiselle*,' he said.

'I'll do that.' Polly stood up immediately, relieved to have something to do at last, and gave Jules a little shake. 'Wake up, Jules, we're going home,' she told him.

It was nearly dark when the taxi put them down before an apartment block in a district of Paris that Polly didn't know at all. She paid the driver and stood looking up at the large, modern building. It had a luxury look from the outside and didn't seem to fit in with Madame's story of near-poverty imposed upon the family by Jules's close-fisted uncle.

'This is your home, Jules?' She looked down at the boy beside her.

'*Oui*,' he said listlessly.

'And your mother will be home by now?'

There was no reply, and Polly leaned down to look into his face by the light of the lamp over the entrance doorway. 'Jules—will your mother be home, do you think?'

He shook his head. 'Maman has gone away,' he said stonily.

This was a facer. Polly felt like saying, 'Why didn't you tell me before?' but of course that would have been absurd. Jules was a strange little boy and she had an idea that he was more shocked by what had happened than he had shown. 'Come along then, let's go inside. Will you show me the way?'

A lift took them up to the third floor and Jules led Polly to a door along a passage on the left. She put in the key she had been given and pushed the door open.

It led straight into a long living room. The first surprise was that all the lights were switched on. The second surprise was the tall man who raised himself quickly from a chair on the far side of the room when they entered.

Polly felt her inside cramp with something like fear. This was Jules's uncle. The man who had quarrelled with Madame Brunet outside the coach this morning (it seemed like days ago!). The sinister figure who had ruined his brother's marriage and now wanted to kidnap his nephew and take him back to England. In a flash the whole story that Madame had so dramatically told on the way to Chartres ran before Polly's eyes like a cinema film.

And the man advancing on her across the room was the villain of the story.

He looked it too, she thought, and her mouth went dry. He was huge, well over six feet and broad with it, and so dark and forbidding that she began to shiver. The near-black eyes glittered under hooded lids and the long, firm mouth was drawn down into an expression of angry frustration.

Polly felt like making a dash for it, but now that she had gone this far she couldn't just walk out and leave Jules to the mercy of this man. Anyway, what was he doing here? This was Madame Brunet's apartment and she had Madame Brunet's key. He must have broken in.

Polly had once heard that attack is the better part of defence, and being brought up in a children's home had taught her to stand up for herself. She said as coldly as she could, speaking in English because she knew from Madame Brunet that he *was* English, 'This is Madame Brunet's apartment. May I ask what you're doing here?'

He ignored her words completely as he came nearer. She was icy cold now and her heart was thumping so violently she thought she would pass out, but somehow she managed to stand her ground. Then he was almost on top of her, furious dark eyes boring down into her soft blue ones.

He was so close that when he spoke the deep, threatening voice vibrated through her head. 'Who the hell are you?' He threw the words at her. 'And what do you think you're doing with my nephew?'

CHAPTER TWO

POLLY retreated backwards a couple of steps and felt Jules draw closer against her. She fought down a horrid sense of alarm. What could he do to her with Jules there?

The man put a hand out, and she flinched, but he was addressing the boy and his voice was a trifle softer as he said, 'Hullo, Jules. Don't you remember me? I'm your Uncle Piran.'

Jules only response was to draw further back behind Polly, from where he peered out at this intimidating stranger, like a frightened two-year-old.

The man shrugged and turned to Polly again. 'Well, what have you to say?' he rapped out.

She looked straight into the dark, glittering eyes, swallowed, and said stiffly, 'Madame Brunet has been involved in a road accident in Chartres. She's been taken to hospital and I understand she's undergoing an operation. At the hospital's suggestion I offered to bring Jules home. I naturally expected to find his mother here?' Her voice rose questioningly.

'His mother is——' he paused, glancing down at the boy '——not here. Nor will be, I imagine,' he added dryly.

His eyes moved over Polly, taking her in from head to foot, taking in the long, slender legs in their tight jeans; the thin white blouse with the frills that fell softly over her rounded young breasts; the wheat-fair hair that curved round her ears and fell to her shoulders. Something that felt like fear stirred uncomfortably in Polly's stomach as she became aware

25

of the sheer masculine strength of the man. He had a
light jacket over the checked shirt now, but it did
nothing to disguise the whipcord muscles beneath. As
his gaze travelled over her she felt the blood rising
hotly into her cheeks.

He saw her embarrassment—of course he did, the
brute—and a faint smile (or was it a sneer?) touched
his long mouth. But he merely said, 'You're English?'

'Yes,' she said through tight lips.

'And your name?' He sounded like one of the
French policemen who had interrogated her, only
more officious.

'Does it matter?' she said coldly.

The dark, thick brows rose again and he said
irritably, 'Of course it bloody well matters! I must
know who Jules has been with all this time.'

He made it sound as if she might have some
infectious disease, or was likely to lead his nephew into
a den of vice.

She lifted her small, firm chin. 'My name is Polly
West,' she said. 'What's yours?'

For a moment he looked taken aback, then he said,
'St Just. Piran St Just.'

Piran St Just—that rang a bell somehow, but she
couldn't think where she had heard the name.

He was speaking again, impatiently. 'Well then,
Polly, if you will please give me any information you
have about Madame Brunet and the name of the
hospital, I won't trouble you further.'

That suits me, Polly thought, the sooner I get away
from this overbearing individual the better. And he
had called her 'Polly' so patronisingly, as if she had
been some inferior in his employment.

She told him briefly all she knew and he jotted
down the details. Then he took out his cheque-book.
'You must let me cover your expenses, Miss West.

Train fares and so on.' He glanced at her, pen poised. 'And something for yourself, of course. For your trouble in this unfortunate matter.'

Polly stared at him. 'You're offering to *pay* me? To give me a *tip*?' Her voice rose several tones.

He sighed. 'Why not?' he said impatiently. 'Why be huffy about it? I wouldn't want you to be out of pocket on our account.'

She went on staring for several seconds more. The man was incredible! It would have given her great pleasure to smack that superior expression from his face, but the occasion hardly called for that. The obvious thing to do was simply to walk out of the room, but Jules was still clutching her arm. She disengaged herself gently from his hot little fingers and gave him a push forward. 'There you are, Jules, you'll be all right now. Your uncle will look after you.' She wished she could believe it. She wished there was something more she could do for the little boy, but there was nothing. She was a complete stranger in a situation that did not in the least concern her.

She nodded coldly to the man. 'I prefer not to take money from you, Mr St Just. If there's anything more I can do, please let me know. The police have my name and address in England, of course.'

She turned to Jules, who was standing quite still, looking from one to the other of them apprehensively, a forlorn little figure. 'Goodbye, Jules. I hope your grandmother will soon be better.'

The boy hadn't said a word or made a sound since they came through the door, but he made up for his silence now. He leapt at Polly and hung on round her waist. 'No, no, *mademoiselle*, you're not going to leave me!'

She stroked his dark hair gently. 'But I must go, Jules. I'm going back to England tomorrow morning and I have to go back to my hotel and pack my bag. You'll be quite all right with your uncle now, and your grandmother will soon be home again.'

Jules yelled, 'I don't want my uncle and I don't want my grandmother! I want you!'

The man stepped forward and put a hand on the boy's shoulder. 'Come along, Jules, we'll have a meal together and get to know each other. And then you can look at television if you like.'

He might not have spoken. Jules continued to cling on to Polly, his face buried in the frills of her white blouse, which, by now, was looking very much the worse for wear. He was crying in great choking sobs that racked his small body.

Over his head she met the St Just man's eyes. 'He's had a bad shock,' she said apologetically, although why she should feel she had to apologise for the boy's behaviour she really didn't know.

The man stood frowning down at his nephew. 'You'll have to toughen up a bit, my lad,' he growled. 'The St Just men don't snivel, you know. Come along, let Miss West go.'

Jules didn't hear, or if he did he took no notice. He continued to hang on to Polly, crying unrestrainedly.

What now? Polly's mind went into a flat spin, remembering all that Madame Brunet had told her about this man—that he was trying to kidnap Jules and take him to England, away from her, and away from his mother. And where was his mother? Madame had said that she was 'no longer able to look after him.' Jules himself had said that his mother had 'gone away.' The St Just man had hinted that she wouldn't be coming back. It was a mystery. Was she suffering from some incurable illness? Had she taken a job that necessitated her being away from Paris—travelling, maybe? Whatever it was, there seemed nobody, now, who could stop this horrible man from doing what he pleased with Jules.

She had a wild idea of going to the police, but if she did, what could she say to them? Even if her French had been up to it she doubted whether she could explain her suspicions. No, she would have to leave poor Jules to take his chance. The St Just man wouldn't actually ill-treat him, somehow she was sure of that. She remembered how he had put his hand quite gently on Jules's head this morning in the coach, and the friendliness of his welcome just now. Not that Jules had responded in the slightest degree. If this man were his uncle he simply didn't want to know.

As the boy clung and sobbed she looked up at the man standing beside them, both hands plunged into his pockets, a picture of angry frustration. 'Well, what do we do now?' she said.

'God knows, this is something I didn't bargain for.' He gave her a look she couldn't interpret. 'There's only one way out as far as I can see, Miss West. If he won't let you go without screaming the building down, you'll have to stay.'

'*Have* to?' she queried. Her blue eyes sparkled frostily.

The dark brows lifted. Then, for the first time, the faintest of smiles touched that long, hard mouth. 'Do I have to go down on my knees and plead with you?'

She said coolly, 'I don't see that happening. But I don't *have* to do what you tell me, Mr St Just. I imagine you're very good at giving orders, but I'm not very good at taking them.'

'Hm.' He looked hard at her. 'Well, Miss West,' he said with heavy irony, 'can I persuade you to give up a little of your valuable time to assuage the fears of a small boy?'

'And get his uncle out of a jam?' she said, with what

she hoped was similar irony.

'All right, all right,' he burst out irritably. 'Have it your own way. Will you stay or won't you?'

Jules had stopped howling but was sobbing silently, his whole body shaking. He was still clinging on to her, but more weakly now. If she exerted a bit of strength she could easily disengage herself and hurry away from the apartment and the whole extraordinary adventure.

The man was waiting for an answer, just standing there, dark and formidable, and yet, in the circumstances, helpless. Almost as helpless as Jules, in a different way.

She sighed. 'All right, I'll stay. Just for an hour or so, to get him settled down. And the first thing is to get some food into him. All he's had since this morning is a drink of lemonade and a bar of chocolate at the station. I didn't want to wait to have a meal, I wanted to get him home as soon as possible. Shall I look around and see what's in the larder?'

He shrugged. 'You can look, you won't find much. I've already looked and most of what I found has gone down the waste chute. Unfit for human consumption. There's a fair amount of gin,' he added with a cynical twist of his mouth. 'I imagine that's Madame's favourite tipple.' He moved towards the door. 'You have a look round and I'll go out and buy some provisions.'

The door closed behind him with a snap and Polly was left alone with Jules, who quickly became a changed little boy now that he knew she wasn't going to leave him.

Polly said, 'You'll have to show me where everything is. Suppose we go and wash our hands and faces first. I feel rather grubby, don't you?'

Grubby was the right word for the bathroom, too.

Expensively fitted in pink, with multiple mirrors and a shower-curtain covered with pink and blue fishes, it would have looked quite pleasing if it had been cared for. Instead, it was a mess. Rows of bottles and pots stood on the windowsill, most of them without their tops, so that their contents had dribbled over the top and run gooily down the side. The pink bath had a grey ring half-way up and the washbasin was blocked and had a sliver of soap disintegrating in the murky dregs at the bottom.

Polly shuddered and turned on the cold tap of the bath. She swilled her face and hands and dried them on a tissue from her handbag. 'Let's do you now, Jules,' she suggested. 'Or would you rather wash yourself?'

'Of course,' he said with dignity. 'I always do.'

He washed quite carefully and dried on a towel that hung limply behind the door. After that he showed her round the apartment.

'This is my room,' he told her, leading her into a fair-sized room with two beds. 'I used to share with Grand'maman,' he explained, 'but when Maman left Grand'maman took her room. I like it better when I'm alone,' he added. 'I can read a lot.'

He opened a cupboard to show her rows of books, stacked up one on top of the other. 'These were my daddy's books,' he said proudly. 'Now they are mine, unless——' he caught his lower lips with his teeth '——unless Grand'maman sells them. Sometimes when I'm naughty she says she'll sell my books.'

Polly said, 'Oh, I'm sure she won't. Keep the door tight shut and then she'll forget all about them.' She wished she could believe it.

'Do you want to see Grand'maman's room?' Jules enquired, and Polly shook her head. If it was anything like the rest of the apartment she would prefer not to.

The state of the kitchen wasn't any better than that of the bathroom. Again, it was adequately equipped, but everything was dull and neglected, and the smell of stale food when she opened the fridge was nauseating. The St Just man had, as he said, emptied the fridge, but it would need a good clean-out to remove the smell of stale cheese and sour milk and other items which would for ever be nameless.

'We have our meals in here,' Jules told her, and Polly glanced towards the plastic-covered table in the corner and said quickly, 'I think it would be nicer to eat in the living-room tonight, don't you? Let's set a table there and have it all ready for when your uncle brings back the food.'

She led the way into the large room. It smelled stuffy and dusty, but at least it was an improvement on the kitchen. There was a folding table in the window and she pulled out the legs and searched in the drawers of the chiffonier for a cloth and cutlery.

Jules was standing behind her, silent. When she turned, with a smile, he said, '*Mademoiselle*,' in a strained little voice.

'Yes, Jules.'

'Is that man going to stay here?'

'He's your uncle, Jules. You'll be able to have lots of fun together.' Well, it was possible, she thought, *just* possible. He *might* not be as grim as he seemed. 'Your uncle Piran,' she added feebly.

Piran. That was the name of a Cornish saint, wasn't it? Anything less saintly than Piran St Just she could hardly imagine. 'I expect he'll enjoy looking after you while your grandmother is away,' she added with an encouraging smile, but her heart sank. What would he do? Whisk Jules away to England with him? There didn't seem much to stop him now, provided he could get over the rules and regulations for taking a child out of the country. And no doubt he had that matter taped already.

'I don't want him to look after me,' Jules stated definitely. 'I can look after myself.'

Polly went down on one knee and gave him a little hug. 'Darling, do you really think you could? How about the shopping, and the cooking and everything?'

'I can shop,' he said stubbornly. 'And I wouldn't need to cook. 'I'd eat sausage and fruit and milk.'

'H'm, not such a bad diet,' Polly agreed, 'but you might get a bit tired of it, don't you think?'

'Well, *you* could do the cooking, *mademoiselle*,' he announced.

Oh dear, this was becoming very awkward. But before Polly could think of a reply that wouldn't raise his hopes too much the door of the apartment flew open and Piran St Just appeared, his arms full of provisions.

He dumped them on the table. 'Sausage, cheese, bread, butter, coffee, milk, fruit. And this.' He pulled the wrapping from a litre bottle of red wine. 'This should cheer things up a little. Somehow I don't fancy drinking Madame's gin.'

He grinned encouragingly at Jules. 'Come along, old man, tuck in. I bet you're starving!'

Jules turned his back. 'No, I'm not,' he said sulkily.

The man slanted an angry glance at Polly, as if this were her fault, and she said quickly to the little boy, 'I think you're rather tired, Jules. How about getting into bed and I'll bring you some supper on a tray and you can read one of those lovely books you showed me.'

'Oh yes, *mademoiselle*, I'd like that,' he said eagerly. He glanced quickly at his uncle and then away again. 'Can I go now?' he said, as if he recognised that this man would have to be obeyed. But he certainly wasn't going to give an inch more than he had to.

The man shrugged. 'O.K. Run along, then,' and Jules shot out of the room without further ado.

Polly hesitated. 'I was just setting the table in here. The kitchen's too awful for words.' She wrinkled her small, straight nose.

'I've seen it,' he said darkly. He slumped down in a chair and closed his eyes.

Polly stood looking at him, taking in the dark, masculine strength in every line of his face. Very male, she thought, and certainly very chauvinistic too. He had been out to buy food and that was all he was prepared to do. The rest was up to her.

She shrugged and went back to the kitchen. Here she found a tray and arranged it with sausage, buttered bread, a ripe peach and a cup of milk.

Jules was already sitting up in bed, in pink-striped pyjamas that looked as if they could do with a wash. Polly felt angry. What a dump of a place this was—no sort of place to bring up a child in.

'Oh, *merci, mademoiselle*.' He took the tray on his knees and put the book he was reading down on the bed beside him. 'I have a book all about Chartres Cathedral. See?' He patted it lovingly. 'My daddy told me all about the cathedral once, a long time ago. And he told me I could be an architect when I grew up,' he added proudly.

'That's a splendid idea,' Polly said warmly. 'Now, you eat up all your supper and then I'll come and see you and say goodnight.'

Back in the living-room she put plates and knives on the table and spread out the food in the middle. She looked at the crusty bread and yellow butter and felt as if her inside were dropping out with hunger. She glanced doubtfully at the man in the chair. He seemed to be asleep.

'Food's ready,' she announced loudly.

He started, opened his eyes, and blinked at her uncertainly. 'What the—— oh yes, of course. You're Miss West, my nephew's guardian angel.' Again the heavy irony.

'And you,' Polly returned lightly, sitting down at the table, 'are Jules's wicked uncle.'

He sat up, scowling. 'What the hell gave you that idea?'

'The wicked uncle bit? Oh, that was Madame Brunet.' She cut off a slice of bread and buttered it thickly. 'I was regaled with your sins all the way to Chartres this morning.'

He levered himself out of his chair and joined her at the table. 'I see,' he said slowly. 'I trust you were entertained.'

'Oh, vastly entertained,' Polly said airily. 'This bread's delicious. Shall I cut you a slice?'

He took the knife out of her hand and held it as if he were thinking of carving up someone, or something, apart from the loaf. 'That bloody woman!' he said savagely, and said no more until he had eaten four slices of bread and a hefty piece of sausage.

Polly tucked in too. She was very, very hungry and the food was delicious. The peaches were heavenly, full of flavour and juice. She ate two of them.

Piran St Just took a formidable folding-knife from his pocket, and selected a corkscrew from among its array of tools. He opened the bottle of wine and as the cork popped he looked across the table at Polly. 'Glasses?' he queried.

Oh no, Mr High and Mighty, I'm not going to run around at your bidding. She pretended not to hear and he said it again, 'Did you find any glasses?'

'I didn't look,' she said.

'Well, go and look now, there's a good girl.'

'I'm not——' she began furiously.

He was studying her face. 'You've got juice running down your chin,' he said.

Muttering under her breath, she threw back her chair and retreated to the kitchen, where she peered into a cracked mirror on the wall and cleaned up her chin. Then she selected the thickest tumbler she could find and carried it back, thumping it down on the table.

He raised dark brows. 'Temper!' And then, 'But you've only brought one glass.'

'I don't want any wine,' she said rather sulkily. He had made her look an idiot and she hated him.

'Rubbish,' he said. 'I can't drink alone. Perhaps you'd like to share my glass?' he added silkily.

Oh dear, she didn't like the way he said that. While he was slanging her she felt safe, but now——➤

He was looking across the table at her in a lazy, amused way and it was doing something very odd to her breathing.

'Of course not,' she said crossly. 'I just don't want any wine.'

He poured out half a tumblerful of the rose-coloured liquid and took a long swig of it. Then he held the glass between his two hands and stared at her over the rim. 'Scared?'

The dark, hooded eyes were lethal. 'Of w-what?' she stammered.

'Of me, of course. The wicked uncle.'

'Oh, don't be silly,' she said, standing up. 'I'll just go and see if Jules is settling down. Then I'll take my leave of you, Mr St Just.'

He shrugged. 'Suits me.' Of course he wanted to get rid of her. He'd been amusing himself, baiting her, making her feel embarrassed. Sadist! she fumed inwardly. Beast. Kidnapper.

She went back to Jules. Only a large peach stone

remained on his plate. He was leaning back against the pillow, balancing a book against his raised knees. The light was very bad and his eyes were drooping, but he opened them wide as Polly went into the room. 'I enjoyed that,' he said politely. '*Merci, mademoiselle.*'

She lifted the tray off the bottom of the bed. 'I think you're ready for sleep now, Jules. Shall I tuck you up and put the light out?'

He yawned, smiled at her angelically and surrendered the book. She put it on the dressing-table and he snuggled down in the bed. He looked very small and rather forlorn under the bedclothes, and Polly felt a pang. She had only known the child a few hours, but something about him pulled at her emotions. She stooped and kissed him. 'Goodnight, Jules.'

'Goodnight, *mademoiselle.*' He looked very sleepy now. 'Tomorrow I'll show you my book and we can look at the pictures of all the things we saw in the Cathedral.'

Tomorrow, Polly thought, she would be on the plane, flying back to England. She said nothing, but it was as if he read her mind. Suddenly he was wide awake, sitting up in bed. 'You're not going away, *mademoiselle*?' he quavered. 'You won't leave me with—that man?' He must have seen the uncertainty in her face. 'You *promised!*' he wailed.

Polly sat on the edge of the bed and took one of his hands in both her own. 'Listen, Jules, you're growing into a big boy now, and soon you'll be a man. So you must be brave and grown-up.' That old stuff! He must have heard it dozens of times before.

'Yes.' He wasn't really listening, 'But you *will* be here in the morning when I wake up, won't you?'

'Darling,' she said, on a rueful little laugh, 'I've got to go back home to England tomorrow. I've booked

my ticket on the plane.' It might have been easier to
lie to him, but she couldn't. Polly believed in telling
the truth whenever it was humanly possible, especially
to children.

Jules's eyes suddenly fixed themselves on a spot
over her shoulder, and Polly knew, without looking,
that the St Just man had come into the room and was
standing behind her.

'I've booked my flight,' she said again, rather
helplessly. For some reason she was quite unable to
look round. She stared at Jules and he stared over her
shoulder at his uncle, and for a long moment there was
silence in the room. Then the man spoke, in that deep
peremptory voice that vibrated through Polly's head.
'What's a flight booking?' he said. 'Cancel it.'

She spun round, the breath catching in her throat.
Never, even in the children's home, where discipline
was strict, had she been ordered about in this
masterful fashion.

'Of course I can't——' she started to say heatedly at
the very moment that Jules squealed. 'Oh, please, you
mustn't go!'

'There you are,' said Piran St Just. 'Two to one.'

'Look,' Polly glared at him, 'this is ridiculous,
and——'

'Now listen, Polly,' he interrupted smoothly, 'before
you start getting on that high horse of yours, consider
the thing reasonably. Jules and I are both inviting you
to stay and help us out of a slight difficulty, aren't we,
Jules?'

For the first time the boy bestowed a look upon his
uncle that was decidedly approving. *'Oui, oui.'* In his
excitement he slid into French nodding his head up
and down. *'Restes-toi, je te prie, mademoiselle.'*

Piran St Just leaned his back against the door and
folded his arms. 'There——' he smiled his ironic smile

'——you can't resist that, can you—*mademoiselle*?'

He was putting on the charm now, of course. He didn't want to be left alone with a fractious child. 'What time's your flight?' he asked.

'Three o'clock,' she told him reluctantly.

'Right. Then I can ring in the morning and cancel it. The phone here doesn't seem to be functioning.' He added as an afterthought, 'You don't *have* to be back tomorrow? You're not being met?'

Off guard, she said, 'Well, no.' What was she going back to, anyway? A room for the night in a cheap hotel. Then—to sit down and figure out what she was going to do next, how she was going to get a job, how long her meagre finances would last out. 'No,' she said again, 'But this is all so—so——'

'Irregular?' he suggested.

'Well, isn't it?' She spread out her hands. 'This morning I didn't even know that you existed, or Jules, or Madame Brunet, and now——'

'—now you seem to be involved with us. That's life, isn't it? Welcome the unexpected and you'll never be bored. Always something new to intrigue one.'

'*Should* I be intrigued?' Unwisely, she met his eyes, those dark, hooded eyes full of ironic amusement, and she had a weak, sinking feeling inside. She was no match for this man and never could be.

'Well, aren't you? Admit the truth.'

She turned her eyes to Jules, who was sitting up in bed taking all this in with great interest. She wondered how much he was aware of the tension between herself and his uncle.

She said, 'Jules and I are friends, aren't we, Jules?' smiling at him.

Piran St Just laughed aloud. 'I think we've won, old boy,' he said. 'I think you can look forward to seeing Mademoiselle in the morning when you wake up.'

Jules bounced up and down on the mattress. '*Bon!* Can she sleep in that bed over there where Grand'maman used to sleep?'

'We'll have to see about that,' said his uncle. 'Now off you go to sleep. Goodnight.'

Jules snuggled down obediently. '*Bonne nuit, mon oncle,*' he said rather shyly. And then '*Bonne nuit, mademoiselle.*'

Polly kissed him, pulled up the covers, turned out the light, and followed Piran St Just back into the living-room. Here she sank into a chair, exhausted. Piran St Just stood looking down at her in silence. Then he went across to the table and poured out some of the red wine and brought it to her. 'Drink this,' he said in a tone that allowed of no refusal. 'You look as if you need it. It isn't exactly what I would prescribe, but it's better than Madame Brunet's gin.'

Polly was too tired to argue. As she drank from the glass she was acutely aware that his lips had touched the same glass only a short time before. It gave her a very strange sensation of—what?—almost of intimacy, and she shivered, so that the glass clattered against her teeth.

'Are you cold?' the man said. 'I'll see if I can get this heating to work.'

He began to fiddle with the regulator on the central heating, but Polly said, 'No, really, I'm not cold—just tired, I think. It's been quite a day.'

He was wandering round the room, looking into cupboards. At last he pulled out a small bar electric fire. 'This will be better than nothing. The heating probably is centrally controlled through the whole building and hasn't come on yet. I'll see the *concierge* about it in the morning.'

The electric fire gave out a cheerful warmth from its one bar. Polly rubbed her hands together. 'That's nice. I think I must have been cold after all.'

'Not surprising.' Piran St Just pulled up a chair close to hers and said, 'Now, if we're going to spend the night together, perhaps we should get to know each other a little better.'

Polly gasped. He couldn't possibly mean what his words suggested. Or could he? Was he the kind of man to proposition a girl he had only just met? 'You're not suggesting——' she began.

He held up a hand in protest. 'I'm not suggesting anything. Perhaps I didn't phrase that too tactfully. Although——' the dark eyes narrowed in amusement '——I'm not saying that any offer would be refused. It's going to be quite a cold night.'

Polly felt a wriggle of fear. What an idiot she had been to let herself in for this, even to help Jules. She knew she was out of her depth completely with this man St Just. He was a sophisticated man of the world and he made her feel young and naïve. But if she was innocent she certainly wasn't ignorant. If he made a determined pass at her she could still walk out, she assured herself. In spite of all the dreadful things Madame Brunet had said about Piran St Just Polly didn't think he was the kind of man who would start an unpleasant scene. All the same, she sat up and put both hands on the arms of her chair, in readiness for instant flight if it became necessary.

'There won't be any offer,' she said coldly. 'I agreed to stay only because of Jules, I think you know that, Mr St Just.'

He was studying her face as she spoke and he was silent for a moment when she had finished. Then he nodded. 'Yes, I *do* know,' he said, and he spoke seriously and without irony. 'I was only teasing— trying to lighten the atmosphere a bit. But I still think we ought to find out a little about each other. God

knows what impression you've got of me from
Madame Brunet, but you won't condemn me on the
evidence of one witness, surely? Ask me anything
you'd like to know and I'll do my best to answer
honestly.'

A fight was going on inside Polly. In one way she
didn't want to know anything at all about this man;
she didn't want to involve herself with him for a
moment longer than was necessary. All she wanted
was to be sure that Jules was going to be happy with
him. Or at least not desperately unhappy. In another
way—well, she was aware of a curious interest to know
the truth about him, and she was fairly sure that she
hadn't heard the whole truth from Madame Brunet.

At last she said, 'Well, there's one thing I'd like to
know. What do you intend to do about Jules?'

'That's easy,' he said. 'I intend to take him back to
my home in England, as soon as I can get the
formalities put through. Tomorrow morning I shall go
and see the British Ambassador and find out exactly
what they are. When I get Jules home I shall make
sure he's properly looked after.'

Looked after by his wife, no doubt! Polly had a
fleeting picture of Mrs St Just. Smooth, beautifully
dressed, haughty—and as sophisticated as he was
himself.

She said, 'You're proposing to take Jules away from
his home and his mother?'

'His home?' The dark brows rose contemptuously as
he glanced round the grimy room. 'What sort of home
is this for a boy? You've seen the way he has to live.
You've seen the kitchen—the bathroom—the lot.
Would *you* consider this a good place to bring up a
child in?'

'Well, no,' Polly had to admit. 'But it's one thing to
take him away from a not very desirable background,

and quite another to remove him from the care of his mother and grandmother.'

The dark angry look was back in his face. 'I hardly think he'll miss his mother—or she him,' he added. 'She hasn't seen much of him for the last two years, since his father died.' A bitter note crept into his voice.

'She doesn't live here, then?'

'She comes and goes. That is, she goes when she finds a man with money who'll give her what she considers a good time. She comes back when he gets tired of her, as they always have, up to now. This time, however, she seems to have caught a man permanently. She was married last week and has departed for America. That'—he spread out his hands '—is why I'm here. I was in Italy when the news reached me. I hired a fast car and I drove up here hell for leather.'

If he had been driving all night it would explain why he had looked such a brigand this morning. He had shaved since, Polly noticed, although the dark shadow was just beginning to show again on his square, stubborn chin. His light jacket fitted immaculately and his rough hair had been brushed, but he still looked like a brigand. Not a man to give up something that he wanted. But he might not find it so easy to win this particular game, Polly guessed.

She said, 'I suppose his grandmother has been the one to look after Jules since your brother died?'

'That,' he said darkly, 'is what I intend to put a stop to. That woman is about as fit to look after a child as—well, if you could meet her daughter, Jules's mother, you'd know what I mean. There's only one thing that Madame Brunet is interested in—money.'

Polly began to get the picture. If this man was telling the truth, then Jules would certainly be better off in a settled home. But children are conservative little creatures and they fear change. Especially, she thought, Jules would. He must have had a good many shocks and changes already in his short life. Like I had, she thought, remembering. Perhaps that was why she felt so warm and sympathetic towards the boy. Polly, too, had lost her father, and her mother had— well, she didn't want to think about her mother now.

'I think you may have difficulty in getting him to go away with you,' she said. 'You can't very well kidnap him, can you?'

'Is that what Madame told you I meant to do?'

She smiled faintly. 'You're not exactly Madame's favourite person. I gathered that from our conversation on the coach.'

He nodded grimly. 'That I can well believe. She isn't mine, either.'

'All the same,' Polly said, 'I think we should phone the hospital and find out how she is.' She had a chilling feeling that he wouldn't be sorry if the news was dire.

He groaned, but he got up out of his chair. 'I suppose you're right. I'd better go out and look for a phone that's working.'

Polly said, 'Would you like me to go?'

He gave her a dark look. 'No, I wouldn't. You might not come back.'

She said indignantly, 'Of course I would have come back. I promised to stay tonight.'

'Yes, I know you did.' He looked down at her, darkly cynical. 'But I'm afraid my experience of women's promises doesn't encourage me to take them too seriously.'

'That's a pity,' Polly said matter-of-factly, 'because when I make a promise I keep it. But you're not to know that, are you, Mr St Just, because you don't know me. All right, *you* go. Although——' a wicked twinkle came into her eyes '—how are you going to be sure I'll be here when you get back, if you're so beastly suspicious?'

He frowned. 'You have a point. I tell you what, we'll both go. You look in and make sure that Jules is asleep.'

She didn't move. 'Please?' she said.

She thought he looked faintly startled. Then a smile pulled at his long, sardonic mouth. '*Please*, Miss West, if you can spare a moment, will you look in and see if Jules is asleep?'

She nodded her acknowledgment coolly, walked over and peeped into the darkened bedroom. Jules was indeed asleep. He looked happy and peaceful, his cheeks flushed and a lock of dark hair straggling across his forehead. Asleep, he looked more like his uncle than ever. Polly wondered how the man out there would look when he was asleep. Would the cynical, world-weary look smooth away? Quickly, she went out and closed the door. 'He's fast asleep, Mr St Just,' she said.

'Good. We'll go, then. And by the way, don't you think the "Mr" is rather formal for two people who've been thrown together as we have? My name's Piran.'

'Celtic?' Polly enquired as they walked down the stairs together.

He glanced back over his shoulder. 'Not many people cotton on to that.'

It was quite absurd that she should feel a tiny glow of satisfaction. So far he had treated her as a lesser form of life—useful in her own small way, but in the dimwit category as far as he was concerned.

'Early history was my subject,' she said.

They had reached the street now, where the lamplight shone softly through the leaves of the overhanging trees.

'Interesting!' Piran St Just said conversationally. 'And what do you do with your early history? Research? Library work?'

For the first time he seemed to be taking her seriously, and she said, 'I hoped to teach, but it fell through at the last minute. That's why I'm having a holiday in Paris.'

They walked on a little further and then Piran St Just said, 'Ah, here's the phone box, I thought I'd seen one around here.'

They stopped outside the glass-sided cubicle. 'You'd better come in with me,' he said.

Polly looked up at him and was suddenly aware of the sheer hard masculinity of the man. The thought of being close to him in that confined space made her shiver. 'N—no,' she stammered, 'I'll wait outside.'

'You'll come in,' he said, and putting an arm firmly round her he opened the door and pushed her inside, making sure his body was blocking the exit so that she couldn't escape. As he searched for the hospital number she had given him, and felt in his pocket for coins, she was pressed against him and her mouth went dry. She twisted round and tried to concentrate on the scene outside: the traffic, the passers-by. It was so quiet inside the phone box that she was sure he must hear her heart thumping. He probably wouldn't be particularly surprised that she was responding to his closeness. No doubt he had that effect on every girl he met—he must be quite used to it.

But Polly wasn't used to it. Never before had any man had such a devastating appeal to her senses. Not Mike, not any man before.

In her three years at college she had listened to the ravings of the other girls about their boy-friends, and felt pleasingly superior, because she herself had no wish to rush into affairs in the way that seemed expected of her. She had managed to acquire the reputation of being a cool girl. Some of the men avoided her, some were intrigued enough to try their luck, without success. Polly was at college to work, not to experiment with sexual encounters.

Piran St Just put in his coins and dialled, in the sequence demanded in French telephone boxes. As he waited for the number he stretched out an arm casually and drew Polly closer against him. To make sure she didn't make a bolt for it, of course! But making a bolt for it was the last thing Polly was capable of at that moment. She was so close to him that her hair was brushing his chin, her cheek was pressed against the thin stuff of his jacket and she could feel his body warmth through it. In her nostrils was the healthy male smell of the man, and she was beginning to feel dizzy with longing to press even closer to him.

As the number came through he eased his arm a little and she pulled away, her mouth dry, her senses roused to a pitch that was quite alarming. Her knees felt like rubber bands and her whole body was weak and pliant. It was too shame-making, too utterly humiliating that this man should have such a devastating effect on her emotions. She recognised the danger and knew there were only two ways of dealing with it—fight or flight. Any fight wouldn't be with Piran St Just, it would be with herself. So the obvious thing to do was to get away at the first possible moment. Surely by tomorrow Jules should have got over his nervousness of his uncle, and she would book another flight back to England and safety, where those dark, hooded eyes could no longer turn her inside to water.

She closed her eyes while he was speaking to the

hospital, not even trying to understand the gabble of French she could hear faintly from the other end of the line.

At last he thanked whoever it was he had been speaking to, and put the receiver back on its cradle. Then he looked down at Polly with a curious, unreadable expression on his face.

'W—what's the news?' Polly faltered. She had a sudden feeling that Madame Brunet was dead—and that he was glad.

But he said, 'Favourable, I suppose, as far as it goes. The operation seems to have gone off successfully, but they're not sure yet about possible further internal injuries. It certainly looks as if Madame is in for a long stay.'

Polly nodded. 'I see. I suppose that suits you very well.'

He was looking enigmatic. 'That depends.'

'Depends?' she echoed idiotically. Why was he still standing there in the phone box, so devastatingly close? 'Depends on what?'

He smiled and she could actually feel her toes curling inside her sandals.

'On you, Polly,' said Piran St Just.

CHAPTER THREE

'*WHAT?*' gasped Polly. 'Why does it depend on me?'
But she knew why, she had had a horrid feeling for the
last half-hour that it wasn't going to be easy to get out
of this situation.

He pushed open the phone box door with his hip
and led her out into the street, his hand still gripping
her arm. Just as if he were a jailer and she his prisoner,
she thought resentfully.

'Surely it's obvious?' he said. 'You seem to be my
life-support system just at the moment. As you say,
Jules isn't going to be easy to shift and—in spite of
Madame's nasty insinuations—I'm no kidnapper. So if
he's to come quietly it will have to be you to persuade
him. You obviously like children, and you've won his
confidence already. Possibly the fact that you're a little
like his mother has something to do with it. In looks, I
hasten to add. I'm sure you don't resemble her in any
other way.'

'Why are you so sure?' Polly enquired shortly. 'You
don't know a thing about me.'

He roared with laughter. 'My dear girl, do you think
I can't recognise a tart when I see one? And you're
not.'

That should have been a compliment, but for some
reason Polly felt slightly deflated. 'This is a fascinating
conversation,' she said stiffly. 'Tell me what I am,
then, if you're so clever at summing up people at first
glance.'

He didn't reply immediately and they walked on in
silence. This was a quiet, suburban part of Paris; there

49

were few cars and fewer passers-by. The green of a
park glimmered darkly from across the road and the
breeze rustled in the leaves above their heads. Piran
gave Polly's arm a little squeeze and there was a smile
in his voice as he said softly, 'You, Polly, are a nice
girl. I've found that out already.'

A nice girl. Little Polly from the orphanage; fond of
children; easily led. A soft touch, in fact. He'd use me
as long as I was useful, she thought, and then thank-
you-very-much-and-goodbye. No, she'd rather be in
London on her own, looking for a job. Piran St Just
spelled danger. She wasn't in his league.

They went up in the lift to the apartment. There
was no sound from Jules's room, but Polly peeped in
again just to make sure that he was still sleeping. Then
she went back to the living room. Piran St Just was
sitting on the sofa, long legs stretched out. 'Well?' he
said, 'are you willing to help in a good cause?'

She couldn't very well say no straight away. 'What
are you suggesting?' she enquired cautiously.

He patted the sofa beside him. 'Come and sit down
and we'll talk it over.'

She pretended not to see the gesture and sat down
in a small chair opposite. He raised his eyebrows a
fraction and shrugged. He didn't miss a thing, Polly
thought. He could probably read her mind and was
preparing to talk her round.

'I'm not suggesting anything cut and dried at the
moment. Merely that you stay with us and keep an eye
on Jules and keep him happy while I make
arrangements to get him back to England, and make
sure that Madame Brunet is O.K. After all, the old
biddy *is* a sort of relative by marriage, whether I like it
or not. You said you were looking out for a teaching
job—well, this would be the next best thing. What do
you say, Polly?'

Polly looked into the hard face, the hooded dark eyes searching her own, and almost intuitively she realised that this moment was vitally important, that whatever she said might affect her life for a long time to come. She knew that now she was still free to make a decision, but that after the moment had passed she would no longer be free. So, she thought, she had better choose the right path now.

She shook her head. 'I'm sorry, Mr St Just. I'd like to help Jules, but I've got my own future to think of.' She grimaced. 'I haven't any life-support system, you see. I really think I must get back to London as soon as possible and try to find a permanent job.' His eyes were holding hers and doing strange things to her concentration.

'Is that your last word, Polly?' He leaned towards her, elbows on knees. 'Couldn't I persuade you to change your mind? I can't very well plead for myself because I can see that I haven't made an altogether favourable impression on you. But for young Jules— it's perfectly obvious that you've won his confidence. It would mean a lot to him, I'm sure, to have you around for a while.'

'Perhaps,' Polly acknowledged in a small, reluctant voice. 'And I'd like to help him to adjust. But——' she shook her head again '—no, I really can't. I have my plans made and I can't alter them because of a casual meeting.'

He sank back into the depths of the sofa, regarding her with interest now. 'You don't believe in fate, then? You can't see a pattern in everything that happens?'

'Can you?'

'Oh, certainly I can. I think you were meant to sit next to Madame B. on the coach. I think that was the beginning of a pattern and that everything that happened afterwards, today, was intended to happen.

Even you sitting opposite me now, looking faintly disapproving.'

'I could easily come back with "Ships that pass in the night"', she said. 'And anyway, Mr St Just, the answer is still No. Sorry, but No. I must go back to London tomorrow. I'm sure Jules will soon get used to you looking after him.'

He shrugged. 'I see I'll have to accept defeat, then. But it seems a pity.'

Polly felt a quite unreasonable stab of disappointment. Weak, she told herself, that's what you are. You knew it would be crazy to agree, but you somehow wanted the decision taken out of your hands.

She stood up. 'I think I'll go to bed now. I must be up early in the morning to go to my hotel and pack, if I'm to catch the afternoon flight.' She felt in command of things now that she had put the necessary gap between herself and the situation.

He stood up, shrugging ruefully. 'Well, thank you for all you've done, Miss West. You've been a great help. I don't know how we should have managed without you, Jules and I.' He was smiling straight down into her eyes and Polly took the whole force of that look. She tried to turn away, but she couldn't move; his eyes held hers like a magnet.

'Dammit, that's no way to say thank you to a pretty girl,' he said softly, and put both hands on her shoulders. 'Thank you, Polly,' he said again, and he bent down and kissed her lips. It wasn't a sensual kiss, neither was it merely a token of gratitude. For a moment longer than was necessary his mouth was pressed against hers, and she felt as if stars were exploding somewhere round her head.

Then he drew away, and he wasn't smiling. 'Now I've really got something to thank you for,' he said. He gave her a little push towards the door of the room where Jules lay sleeping. 'You'd better go to bed now or I shall forget that you're a nice girl.'

He was fooling, of course, and Polly knew she should quip back, take the kiss as lightly as he had offered it. But her throat was dry and she could say nothing at all. She stared at him for a moment, eyes wide, then she almost ran into the bedroom and closed the door.

She stood with her back to it, breathing unevenly. She had never felt like this before about a man and she didn't know how to cope with it. What was she, for heaven's sake? He had called her a 'nice girl', but nice girls didn't feel like she was feeling now about a man she had only met an hour ago. And a man who almost certainly had a beautiful, soignée wife presiding over an elegant home, where Jules would finally be taken, if Piran St Just's plans materialised.

But she was very tired. She really didn't want to think about the man in the next room, she wanted to get some sleep.

It was dark in the bedroom, but the curtains were thin, and a faint light filtered in from the street outside. Polly groped her way across to the bed opposite Jules's and turned back the duvet. It wasn't going to be a very comfortable night's sleep, she was sure of that. A strange bed, and no nightdress. Also she had forgotten to go into the bathroom to make some sort of attempt to clean her teeth. This worried her for a while, but she couldn't face the effort of returning to the living room to encounter the St Just man again tonight. She would have to pretend she was doing some sort of an Outward Bound exercise and sleep rough. With a sigh she pulled off her sandals and slipped into the bed.

She screamed. And screamed. She couldn't help herself. In the bed something cold and clammy met her bare feet, sending wave after wave of terror shuddering through her whole body. Horrible, obscene memories of slimy animals, seen on TV nature films, presented themselves to her imagination. She was shaking from head to foot and sobbing with sheer terror when Piran St Just threw open the door and took her arms in a steely grip from behind.

She heard his angry voice. 'What the bloody hell's going on? You'll have the *gendarmes* up here if you don't shut up.'

'I—in the b-bed——' Polly whimpered. 'An animal—I think it's dead. It's horrible——'

Again she experienced the nauseating shock when her bare feet encountered that obscene object in the bed and her sobs rose almost into hysteria.

'Be quiet!' Piran shook her roughly and as she began to scream again he slapped her smartly on her cheek.

Her knees gave way under her and she slid down to the floor as he snapped on the light. In a daze she saw him walk over to the bed and she stared in horror as he groped down into it.

'God!' he muttered in disgust. 'Cold—and leaking. The mattress is soaked through. There's your animal, Polly.' He threw a rubber hot water bottle on to the floor beside her.

After a moment she put out a shaking hand and touched it gingerly. 'Ugh! Beastly!' With a tremendous effort she got to her feet. 'Sorry!' she said in a croak. She cleared her throat and tried again. 'That was silly of me, making all that fuss. I'm not usually such a coward.'

'Understandable!' he said, not very sympathetically. He walked quietly across to Jules's bed. 'A good thing he was tired,' he murmured. 'He doesn't seem to have been wakened by all the fuss. Now come along——' he shooed her out of the bedroom. 'You can't sleep in that bed tonight, that's for sure.'

Polly sank down on to the sofa, feeling absolutely whacked now. She didn't care about anything, or any impression she had made. All she wanted was to lie down and sleep. 'I could easily sleep here.' She patted the sofa; it was deep and soft. One of the springs was broken, but she could avoid that. She yawned. 'I— really must sleep somewhere soon,' she murmured stupidly.

Piran St Just lowered himself on to the sofa beside her. 'You've had a shock,' he said. 'You need something to get you out of it first. You think you'll sleep if you just lie down and close your eyes now, but of course you won't. Or if you do, you'll wake up soon with a nightmare. And we don't want any more hysterics, do we?' He put one arm about her shoulders and gave it a little squeeze. 'Poor little Polly,' he said softly. 'What a game we've given you, haven't we? Never mind, you'll be rid of us tomorrow.'

'Yes,' she said in a small voice, and suddenly it seemed terribly sad that she wasn't going to see him again. Or Jules, of course. Stupid tears gathered in her eyes and she bit her lower lip hard, but it was no good. A moment later she was sobbing, and he was holding her tight against his checked cotton shirt.

He let her go on crying, he simply dug in his pocket and produced a handkerchief and stuffed it into her hand. She buried her face in it and it smelled of cologne and laundry-cleanliness, and there was something very comforting and—right—about being held in this man's arms.

Which was odd, because up to now she had always carefully avoided situations where proximity with a man might go to his head—or hers. She didn't want to get involved in any sort of a love affair just yet.

And now here she was with all her good resolutions

tottering. Alone in a flat at night, with a stranger, and feeling warm, and soft, and weak with this treacherous longing to reach up and put her arms round his neck.

Suddenly she heard a muffled sound from inside Jules's bedroom and sat up, wiping her eyes. 'Oh, goodness, I must have wakened him after all.' She jumped to her feet, anxiety allaying her tiredness, and hurried into the bedroom. 'It's all right, Jules dear——' she began.

It was maddening that her silly mistake should have wakened him and upset him. Then she saw with horror that it was more than just an upset. He was sitting up in bed, wheezing and gasping, one hand to his throat, his eyes agonised.

'Oh God!' Polly whispered over her shoulder to Piran, behind her. 'It's an asthma attack.' One of the boys at the home had been inclined to have asthma attacks, especially if anything happened to upset him, and she recognised the symptoms.

'Have a look in all the drawers and see if you can see anything that looks like an inhaler with his name on it,' she said over her shoulder to Piran. She sat on the bed and put an arm round the child, speaking slowly and soothingly to him. 'There, love, you'll soon be better, try to breathe out. Blow on my fingers—there, that's better, that's fine.'

'I can't find anything,' Piran whispered, by her side. Like most men in the face of sudden inexplicable illness, he sounded worried and at a loss.

'All right, then,' Polly said in a low voice. 'This is probably just a stress reaction. He'll be better soon, I'm sure. You go and warm some milk. That will do him good when he's over the attack.'

Piran disappeared promptly. Polly went on comforting the boy, and at last Jules was breathing more easily, lying back against the pillow, looking very white and frail.

Piran came back with some warm milk in a beaker and Jules was persuaded to drink a little. Finally, exhausted, he dropped off to sleep again, breathing more easily, with only a little catch now and again. Polly waited until she was quite sure all was well and then went out of the room, leaving the bedside lamp switched on with its shade tipped away from the sleeping boy.

In the living room Piran was standing in front of the electric fire, hands deep in his pockets, brow creased.

'This is a facer,' he said gloomily as Polly sank wearily into the depths of the sofa. 'We appear to be dogged by bad luck.' He didn't seem to notice that he had said 'we', thus including Polly in the enterprise.

But Polly noticed. She said quickly, 'I don't suppose it's anything to worry about. I said it was asthma, but it may only be a sort of nervous reaction to everything that's happened to Jules recently. I rather think he's one of those children who are inclined to bottle things up, and if he's been anxious inside then this attack would be his way of letting go. There was a little boy at the home who had one of these attacks and once he settled down it wasn't repeated. It probably won't happen again with Jules, either.'

He flicked her a keen look. 'The home?'

'The children's home where I grew up,' she said. 'It was a very good one,' she added. She would hate to give him the 'poor little orphan' impression. And she wasn't going to mention the bad times, either—the sickening feeling of waiting and waiting for the mother who had promised to come back but never came. The terrible black loneliness that came from nowhere and lasted for days. Mostly she had been contented, though, and some built-in cheerfulness in her nature had seen her through. By the time the examinations came along and she was immersed in work the black lonely periods came less and less frequently, until by now they seemed almost to have disappeared. The trick was to get busy, to find something to do, someone to help.

She brought her thoughts back and saw that Piran was watching her closely. 'But we were talking about Jules,' she said. 'As I said, I don't suppose this sort of attack will happen again.'

'Can you promise me that?'

'Well—no, of course I can't.'

'Can you tell me how to deal with it if it does?'

She saw where all this was leading. 'You—you just have to reassure him and—and comfort him until the attack passes off. And you'll let him see a doctor, I'm sure.'

He ran a hand through his hair. 'Can you imagine just how comforted Jules will be—by me?'

When she didn't reply he sat down beside her and said simply, 'I'm in your hands, Polly. Won't you change your mind and stay with us?'

This time there wasn't any choice. Piran St Just would get his way, but not, Polly assured herself, because of his machismo. It was simply because she couldn't, now, desert little Jules.

She sighed. 'I see I'll have to—for Jules's sake, of course.'

He grimaced. 'Of course! I didn't suppose it would be for mine.'

Polly ignored that. She said, 'I'm prepared to stay around and help until you can get Jules back to your home in England. And then your wife will be able to cope, I'm sure.'

The grim look came back into his face. 'That's the trouble—I don't have a wife any more.' He was silent for a moment and then he added bitterly, 'The St Just men don't seem to have had much luck with marriage. Mine ended just under a year ago.'

'I see,' said Polly. 'Well, I suppose you'll be able to get a housekeeper to look after Jules.'

He glanced at her and away again. 'Yes, I suppose so.' He sounded less than enthusiastic. 'Oh well, we can sort that out when we get Jules home.'

'And where is home?' Polly enquired.

'A little village in Dorset, near the sea. You'll like it, Polly.'

'Oh yes?' she enquired coolly. It sounded lovely, but she wasn't going to allow Piran to see that she was impressed. She felt as if she were walking through a minefield. One false step and everything would explode around her.

There was a silence. He sat back in his corner of the sofa, studying her face, and she thought he was waiting for her to make another remark. When she didn't he said briskly, 'Well, we'll have to find somewhere for you to spend the night. Come and have a look in Madame's room.'

She said, 'I—I thought you were going to sleep there.'

'That was the idea,' he said, and she saw he was laughing at her. 'Don't you trust me yet? Do you still think I have—what's a coy way of putting it?—designs on your virtue?'

'I don't know,' Polly said flatly. 'Have you?'

He laughed again, louder this time. 'Oh, Polly, Polly, you're superb! You're as good as a drink of astringent lime-juice.'

'Thank you,' she said again. 'But you haven't answered my question.'

He appeared to ponder. Then he said, 'Would you be offended if I said no?'

'Offended?' Polly burst out. 'Of course I wouldn't.
I'd be reassured. Why should you think I'd be
offended?'

'Most of the girls I've met would, that's all,' said
Piran. 'It seems to be expected of a man that he makes
a pass at a girl. A sort of compliment.'

'Well, I certainly *don't* expect it,' Polly said. This
conversation was getting altogether too intimate for
her liking. 'So let's change the subject, shall we?'

'If you insist,' he said. 'I was just beginning to enjoy
it, but whatever Mademoiselle says. As far as beds go,
you'd better have Madame Brunet's room and I'll kip
down on the sofa here.'

Polly looked at the length of the sofa and then at the
length of the man sitting in the corner of it, and she
started to giggle. 'If you enjoy sleeping jack-knife
fashion I suppose it might do. No, I'll have the sofa—
then I'll be near to Jules and I'll hear him in case he
wakes up again.'

'As you wish. Will you go in and select some
blankets or whatever you need—or can find. I'm going
to make some tea.'

'Oh—tea!' murmured Polly. 'That would be lovely.'

He smiled at her ruefully. 'I set out to charm her
and all she enthuses about is tea! Ah well!' He sighed
heavily and disappeared towards the kitchen.

Polly stood looking after him. She couldn't make
the man out. At first he had seemed like an absolute
horror, and she had a feeling that he could repeat the
performance at the drop of a hat, should things not go
his way. But as things *were* going his way; as she had
agreed, in spite of her misgivings to stay on and help
him out with Jules, then he could be pleasant and
companionable. Fun, in fact.

She shook her head and went into Madame's
bedroom to select a couple of blankets from the large,

untidy bed. There was a duvet too, and *he* could have that. Somehow she couldn't think of him as Piran, much less call him by his name.

She carried the blankets back to the living room and draped them over a chair, as he came back with the tea.

Suddenly Polly wanted to dispel the impression he must have got of her as a timid little nitwit. She wanted him to accept her on her own terms.

'I really am sorry about all the hoo-ha,' she said. 'It was so stupid of me to panic like that, and I feel terrible about upsetting Jules.'

'Couldn't be helped,' he said casually, setting the tray on the floor beside the sofa, and she was sorry she had spoken. Of course, he wasn't really interested in her as a person, only because she could be of use to him. She mustn't forget that.

He sat down and patted the sofa beside him. 'Come on, let's have some tea and forget about all the goings-on of the last half hour. Sit down and be comfy.' This time Polly did as he asked, sinking back against the soft velvet and taking the cup he handed her.

He had made the tea good and strong and soon her spirits started to revive. She put the cup down on the floor. 'That was a super cup of tea. Thank you.'

'One of my more civilised accomplishments,' he told her with a grin. He really was being very charming to her now, but she mustn't relax too much with him yet. Dark suspicions still lurked at the back of her mind, and in any case the charm was no doubt put on to keep her 'sweet'.

She was much too aware of him, lounging there beside her. Out of the corner of her eye she could see the soft pile of his fawn cord trousers, a trifle worn at the knees. If she put out a hand she could stroke them. It would be an invitation, and how would he respond?

Polly was swimming in deep waters. In spite of all that had just happened the magnetism of the man sitting beside her was so powerful that she felt a hunger that frightened her. She needed to curl up against him on the sofa, to feel his arms round her, his mouth on hers. He was so close that it was all she could do not to move and lean against him.

Horrified, she realised that he was watching her, a gleam of humour in the dark, hooded eyes. Could he have guessed where her thoughts were straying? 'I think,' he said in an amused voice, 'that you've had enough excitement for one day. You tuck up on the sofa now and I'll remove myself to Madame's room next door.' He got to his feet. 'Goodnight again, Polly. Sleep well, and wake me if you need any help again with Jules.'

Surprising herself, Polly did sleep well. It was pleasantly warm in the living room and she rolled herself up in the blankets, turned out the light, curled up on the sofa, and was asleep almost immediately.

When she wakened the sun was streaming between the dusty pink velvet curtains. She sat up, shaking off the blankets, aware immediately of where she was and all that had happened.

She heard Piran's voice in the kitchen and, pushing her hair into some sort of order, she went across and looked round the door.

He was standing at the sink, washing a pan, and Jules was putting cups on a tray, carefully, one by one.

Piran turned round, mop in one hand, frying pan in the other. 'Hullo,' he grinned. 'Jules and I are getting breakfast. You were sleeping so peacefully we didn't want to wake you. That's right, isn't it, Jules?'

Jules gave him a guarded look. '*Oui, mon oncle.*' His tone when he spoke to Piran was a little less suspicious than it had been yesterday, but he was still not exactly forthcoming.

When he looked at Polly, however, his small face lit up. '*Bonjour*, Mademoiselle Polly.' He didn't move towards her. What an insecure child he was, Polly thought painfully. She went over and lifted him off his feet and swung him round. '*Bonjour*, Jules. And how are you this lovely morning?'

A look of delight spread over the little boy's face. 'Very well, thank you, Mademoiselle Polly,' he said quaintly. Over his head Polly's eyes met Piran's and he shook his head slightly. She took that to mean that Jules hadn't remembered anything of his attack the previous night. She smiled and nodded. That was a blessing; and it probably meant that the wheezing attack had been just that—an isolated happening brought on by the stress of the day and finally by her own stupid fuss over the hot-water bottle.

This would be a critical time for him. It was quite possible, she knew, for a first attack to be followed by others, until a real asthmatic condition was established. At all costs that mustn't be allowed to happen.

She said brightly, 'What are we having for breakfast, then? I'm very hungry, aren't you, Jules?'

Piran said, 'Some good English bacon and eggs would go down well, but I think we'll have to make do with omelette, if I can get this pan fit to use. Will you make the coffee, Polly, while I struggle with the omelette? I found some eggs and I can only hope they're not just about to hatch out.'

Polly giggled. Suddenly the whole affair had become a rather exciting adventure.

Breakfast was a cheerful affair. Piran had evidently set himself to win Jules's confidence and acceptance. He launched into stories of his home in Dorset, a spot where once the dinosaurs used to live. Jules had a book on dinosaurs, he said eagerly, and trotted off to find it.

'There is a museum near to my home where you can see the bones of some of the dinosaurs,' Piran told him. 'Would you like to see them?'

'Oh yes——' Jules began, and then looked uncertainly towards Polly. 'Will you come too, *mademoiselle*?'

'If I'm invited,' Polly said demurely, without looking at Piran.

'Sure you're invited, we'll all go just as soon as we get home.' He grinned at Jules. 'I thought it would be rather jolly if we all flew back to England in a day or two, Jules. You and I—and Mademoiselle Polly, of course,' he added quickly as the boy's head turned inevitably to her. 'You see, Grand'maman will be in hospital for a long time and there won't be anyone to look after you here.'

Jules forehead creased. Another change, and he would be nervous about that, Polly knew. She smiled at him and said, 'I'd like to see the dinosaur's footprints too. We could go together.'

The eager look that she was beginning to recognise came into the boy's face. Poor child, he had probably been starved of understanding and companionship since his father died. It would be rewarding to watch his mind and interests develop. 'I would like——' he began.

There was a loud knock on the door of the apartment. Piran frowned. 'Who the blazes can that be?' He walked across and opened the door. Two policemen in their blue uniform and peaked caps stood outside.

'Monsieur St Just?' said the taller of the two.

'Yes,' Piran frowned.

The policeman peered into the room to where Polly and Jules sat at the table. 'I would like a word with

you, *monsieur*.' He walked into the room, followed by
his companion.

'What is this?' Piran asked. 'Is it Madame Brunet?
Is she worse?'

The policeman gave a hard, suspicious look. 'It is
indeed about Madame Brunet,' he said, 'but she is not
worse, *monsieur*, indeed she is much improved this
morning.'

'Good,' said Piran unconvincingly.

The policeman cleared his throat. 'May I speak to
you alone, *monsieur*?'

Piran hesitated for a moment, then turned to the
two at the table. 'Will you please leave us for a
moment, Polly—and take Jules with you?'

Polly took Jules's hand and led him into the kitchen
and closed the door. The little boy looked rather
white. 'What do they want now?' he asked nervously,
and Polly guessed that this wasn't the first time that
policemen had come to the apartment.

'I don't know,' she said, 'but I don't suppose it's
anything very important. Let's make some fresh
coffee, shall we?' She managed to keep him busy and
interested until, a few minutes later, the door opened
and Piran, looking grimmer than ever, said, 'Will you
both come back now?'

He took Jules's hand. 'Jules, will you tell these
officers who I am, please?'

Jules blinked, went even paler but said in a precise
little voice, 'You are *mon oncle, monsieur*.'

Piran stared at the policemen, his dark brows raised.
'Quite so. And who better to look after my nephew
while his grandmother is in hospital?' He spoke quite
softly, but there was something in his voice that
brought a slightly uncomfortable expression to the
man's face.

He persevered with his enquiry, however. He went

down on his haunches and smiled benevolently into Jules's face. 'And are you happy here with your uncle, *mon petit*?'

Jules backed away from the large, grinning face and hung on to Polly, gazing up at her with trusting dark eyes. 'Yes, sir,' he replied.

The policeman straightened up with a grunt and looked enquiringly at Piran. 'And may I ask, *monsieur*, what relationship Mademoiselle has to your nephew?' He leered in Polly's direction.

'No relationship at the moment,' Piran replied, at his most arrogant. 'If it has any bearing on the matter I may tell you that quite soon, I hope, she will be his aunt by marriage. Miss West is my fiancée, officer. In case it interests you, we intend to marry almost immediately.' He spoke blandly, and if he heard Polly's quick intake of breath he ignored it.

This announcement evidently tipped the scales with the policeman. Or perhaps it was the smile that Polly had given him when she came into the room. After taking down a few more particulars and asking Piran to report if he intended to move from this address, he wished them all *bonjour* and the two policemen took their departure.

Jules was staring from one to the other of them, and his small face was alight with anticipation. 'Is it so, *mon oncle*?' he asked eagerly. 'Will you marry Mademoiselle Polly very soon? Will she stay with us?'

Piran, still smiling, found Polly's eyes and there was something in his own dark, liquid eyes that took her breath away.

'You know, Jules,' he said seriously, 'I think that's quite an idea.'

CHAPTER FOUR

JULES was dancing up and down with excitement and
Piran put a hand on his shoulder to quieten him.
'Have you finished your breakfast, Jules?' Jules said
that he had, and Piran said, 'Well then, suppose you
go off and find some more books that you'd like to
show me? Mademoiselle Polly and I want to have a
little talk.'

Polly could hardly wait until the door was closed
behind the boy. 'How could you?' she burst out.
'Haven't you involved me sufficiently in all this,
without—without giving information to the police
about me? You really are the most arrogant—
impertinent——' she was bubbling over with rage and
she couldn't think of any words bad enough. 'You're a
menace,' she finished weakly.

To make her even madder Piran had that amused
smile on his lips—the kind of smile he would bestow
upon a little girl with tantrums. 'I'm sorry if you
object to being my fiancée—temporarily,' he said
mildly. 'I thought it was the best way to keep the
gentleman happy. You see, Madame Brunet has been
raising all hell at the hospital, accusing me of every
crime in the book. Knowing Madame, I should think
the police were a bit sceptical, but even so they had to
take her seriously and investigate what was going on
here. I imagine they were quite satisfied. And your
presence—and Jules's obvious devotion to you—
helped a lot.'

'Yes,' said Polly, still seething. 'That's another
thing—almost the worst thing. You've given Jules the

impression that we're about to rush off and get married. What's he going to feel like when he knows you were lying? It won't exactly boost his confidence in you, will it?'

'We'll cross that bridge when we come to it,' said Piran St Just maddeningly. 'Meanwhile, let me remind you that you *have* promised to help.'

'O.K., I promised, but that doesn't give you a free hand to—to——' She was almost in tears.

He put an arm round her shoulders and drew her gently against him. 'Don't worry, little Polly,' he said softly. 'I won't let any harm come to you, I promise. I'm eternally grateful to you for your help.'

He pulled her down on to the sofa beside him, and when he spoke his voice had changed, become intense. 'Polly, listen—I want that boy and I mean to have him. When we were young Maurice and I were very close—that was before he made that appalling marriage. I thought the world of him—our parents were dead and in a way I felt responsible for him, he was so much younger. He would have been devastated if he could have known what would happen to Jules, the way the boy would be neglected. This is something I can do for Maurice—the only thing now—to make sure that his son is brought up as he would have wished. Do you understand?' He turned on her, almost fiercely.

Polly nodded. 'Yes,' she said, 'I do understand.'

He was silent for a time, and she thought he had forgotten she was there. He was staring into the glowing bar of the electric fire, his face dark and moody. Then he said, 'I suppose if I'm perfectly honest I must admit to another reason why I want Jules. I want him for the son I'm not likely to have now.'

'Why ever not?' Polly said calmly. 'Surely you'll

marry again? One mistake needn't put you off for life.'

His mouth twisted. 'With respect, my child, you
don't know what you're talking about. And anyway,
my experience wasn't of one mistake, it was of two.
You're forgetting my brother.' He added bitterly, 'We
both made the same ridiculous mistake—we imagined
that love and marriage go together, as the old song
said. They don't, that's for sure.' He was silent for a
moment, his mouth taking on a hard line. Then he
added, 'At least I suppose I must be grateful that *my*
marriage didn't kill me.'

Polly gasped. 'What are you saying? You don't
mean——'

'Oh no, I'm not talking about anything as dramatic
as murder. Simply that Maurice was never a very
strong boy. He died of neglected pneumonia.'

'And you blame his wife?'

'I blame his wife,' he said quietly and very bitterly.
'She was having an affair with another man when
Maurice became very ill. I don't suppose she even
bothered to get a doctor in until it was too late.'

There was a long silence and Polly could think of
nothing to say. At last she murmured, 'Thank you for
telling me, and I'll help in any way I can. I only
wish——'

'Wish what?'

'Oh, nothing.' She couldn't say, I wish I'd had
someone to care about what happened to *me* when I
was deserted by my mother.'

She drew away from him and stood up. 'All right
then, as you say, we'll play the thing by ear as we go
along. Now, what are the plans for today?'

Piran got to his feet too and drew in a long breath,
letting it out on a sigh, as if he were dispelling some
painful memories. 'Well, first of all,' he said in a
businesslike tone, 'I want to go along to the British

Embassy and make some enquiries. Will you and Jules be happy here until I come back?'

It was a busy morning. Polly decided that the first thing to do was to clean up the apartment, and Jules helped enthusiastically. She found she enjoyed all the washing and dusting and polishing; it was rewarding to see the place begin to shine and sparkle in the sunshine. Jules, at first a little puzzled at what was going on (poor child, he must be quite unaccustomed to anyone doing housework), soon entered into the spirit of the thing, and when Polly stood him on a box and gave him a brush and some powder-cleaner, he scrubbed away at the kitchen sink with a will.

Once the living room, the kitchen and the bathroom had been attended to, the next thing was to buy in some food. The bedrooms could wait until later. Polly looked in her purse and found she had enough francs left for a modest shopping spree. Jules, when asked, seemed a little vague about shopping facilities, so Polly suggested they go out and have a look around.

Downstairs, they encountered the *concierge*, a small woman with a bun of dark hair scraped up on top of her head and wrapped in a voluminous flowered overall. She had the lines on her face that come from a lifetime of hard work and making the best of things with humour and good nature. She patted Jules's head. 'And how is my little cabbage this morning?' She regarded Polly curiously. 'Monsieur St Just informed me that there had been an accident.'

'Yes, unfortunately.' Polly spoke in her best French. 'Madame Brunet has had an operation, and it seems to have been successful, but it may be some time before she is allowed to come home. Meanwhile Jules's uncle and I are looking after the apartment.'

The *concierge* raised her eyebrows, shrugging, and

launched into a flood of rapid French, of which Polly
could only understand a few words here and there.
She got the impression that the woman didn't think
very much of Madame Brunet—or her daughter. She
heard the word Zurich a good deal.

'Madame Brunet does not belong to Paris, then?'
she asked, more to be polite than because it was
important to her.

'*Non, non.*' The woman sounded quite heated. 'She
is not French, that one!' There was quite evidently
some sort of a feud between Madame Brunet and the
concierge, but now she calmed down and, regarding
Jules, whose hand was tightly in Polly's, she sighed,
'*Pauvre petit garçon!* They do not care properly for
him—those women!'

But she bestowed an approving look on Polly
herself, and in answer to her enquiry told her that
there was a market not half a kilometre down the
street, where she could buy anything she needed.

The small market was fascinating, like nothing Polly
had seen in England. The fruit and vegetables, stacked
in colourful mounds, looked mouthwateringly fresh and
she could have spent all her remaining francs on them
alone. But she would have to wait until Piran St Just
doled out some housekeeping money to her. She
contented herself with buying crisp salad leaves,
tomatoes, cucumber, and some more peaches. Jules
expressed a liking for bananas, so those were added.
At the delicatessen stall there were so many kinds of
sausages and pâtés that all Polly could do was point to
the ones that looked the most appetising, and trust to
luck. She bought another *baguette*, crusty and golden,
and a wedge of one of the dozens of different cheeses.
'That should do us for lunch,' she told Jules as they
made their way back.

They walked slowly and Polly looked about her as

they went. This was a very pleasant part of Paris; quiet and leafy, and the apartment houses all looked quite expensive. Evidently Maurice had been able to leave his widow fairly well provided for, which seemed to give the lie to Madame Brunet's wail that her beloved Ninette had been forced to go out to work to support her mother and her son.

Piran had returned by the time they got back to the apartment. He was standing by the window, looking as black as thunder, and he swung round as Polly and Jules came into the room.

'Where the hell have you been? I thought I told you to wait here for me.'

Polly rested her heavy carrier bags on the table. 'Did you?' she said innocently. 'I don't think I could have heard you. Jules and I have been shopping. Come along, Jules, let's go and unload.' She marched past the man and walked calmly into the kitchen.

Piran came after her and stood close behind her at the table, where she was setting out her purchases. He was so close that her heart began to thump with heavy beats, but she kept on with her task. 'I'm sorry, Polly,' he said softly, and after a moment she felt—or thought she felt—his lips touch her hair. But she could have been mistaken. 'It was just that I got back and you weren't here,' he said quietly.

She gave a brittle little laugh. 'Did you think Jules and I had run away?'

'You'd better not,' he growled. 'I want you both here, where I can keep my eye on you.'

She moved away from him then and her hands were trembling as she plunged the salad greens into ice-cold water in the sink. 'That's O.K.,' she said casually. 'And, by the way, you owe me sixty francs, which is about all the currency I have left.'

He took out his wallet and laid a small wad of notes

on the table. 'That's for housekeeping,' he said, 'while we're here. And it looks as if that may be some little time.'

'Oh yes,' said Polly, remembering. 'How did you get on at the Embassy?'

'Slowly,' he said, pulling a wry face. 'Everyone I needed to see was either out or engaged in some lengthy conference. I made an appointment for tomorrow. Meanwhile we may as well amuse ourselves as best we can. What would you like to do, both of you?'

Polly looked at Jules. 'I've been wondering—Jules, shouldn't you be at school? Where is your school?'

He looked from one to the other of them and then down at the carpet. 'Jules,' said his uncle, quite kindly, 'you must tell us where you go to school. You do have a school somewhere, don't you?'

The boy's mouth quivered, as if he were remembering some unpleasant experience. 'Grand'maman sent me to school,' he faltered. 'But I was ill and I couldn't go again.'

'When was that?' Piran insisted. 'When were you last at school?' But Jules shook his head and it was obvious that he either couldn't remember or wasn't going to tell them.

Piran shrugged. 'Oh well, I suppose there's not much point in forcing the issue. We'll do something about it when we get him back to England. We'll just have to hope the authorities don't catch up with us here. I've no idea how strict they are about education and school attendance. I'll clear it up when I see them tomorrow at the Embassy.' He looked at his watch. 'Now, what next? It's too early for lunch. How about collecting your things from your hotel, Polly? I've got my car in the garage here. Come along, the two of you.'

He peeled off his jacket and threw it over the back of a chair. He was brimming over with energy now, exuberant almost. Things were going his way and he was a different man from the dark, lowering individual Polly had encountered—could it only be yesterday? It seemed like weeks that she had known him. Every bit of him was familiar to her—the strong, athletic body, the sunbronzed skin. She knew exactly the way his sloe-dark eyes moved under their lowered lids, taking in everything. She was sure he was like a camera, registering all around him. And his mouth—the finely sculptured lips that could twist in bitter cynicism, but now were grinning with pleasure, like a schoolboy promised a treat. Yes, Polly thought, he would be good for Jules and the boy would quite soon become devoted to him, she was sure of that. And she surprised herself by feeling a prick of something very like jealousy because she wouldn't be there to see it happen.

At the hotel, Piran and Jules waited in reception while Polly packced her bag and handed in the key. She hadn't any bill to pay—it had all been settled in advance when she booked the tour. 'Tips?' questioned Piran, and placed a note on the reception desk.

'*Merci, monsieur.*' He received a look full of awareness from the girl behind the counter, and a brilliant white smile. Polly looked away quickly, suddenly realising that she didn't want to see Piran smiling back at the girl. How pathetic, she scolded herself, to be jealous of a man you hardly know and who is merely making himself pleasant to you because at the moment you are useful to him.

Piran put Polly's two modest travelling bags in the back seat of the car. 'Now,' he said, 'I think we'll go shopping. For one thing you must have an engagement ring, and for the next you'll need some more clothes,

I'm sure, to see you through the rest of the time we're in Paris. You must give me the pleasure of providing you with those.'

Polly opened her mouth to protest, but Piran leaned across Jules, who was sitting between them, and put a hand firmly on her knee. 'This is all quite essential, you know,' he said, glancing down at the boy's dark head, and she realised that he was talking in a sort of code that they both understood but Jules didn't. It didn't make her feel any better, but there was nothing she could do about it. So she sighed and shrugged her agreement. And in fact, Piran St Just was right—she could hardly appear as his fiancée dressed in any of the clothes she had with her.

'We'll leave your bags at the apartment,' he said, 'and then you might like to change, now that we've got your luggage.'

Polly glanced down at her blouse and jeans, which she had worn since she set off for her coach tour to Chartres yesterday morning, and flushed. 'You needn't rub it in,' she said crossly. 'I know I look a wreck, but it's not exactly my fault.'

His hand was still resting on her knee and now he gave it a little squeeze and grinned, 'You would look charming in anything—*ma chérie*.' That compliment, of course, was intended for Jules's benefit, not hers.

'*Merci, monsieur*,' she murmured mockingly. He glanced at her, in a way she couldn't interpret at all, and took his hand away.

Back at the apartment Polly went into Jules's room and closed the door. Here she unpacked her bag again and took out the two dresses that were all she had with her, except for her jeans and a couple of blouses. She hadn't been intending to do anything exciting on this trip and was travelling light.

She chose her favourite of the two dresses—a soft

blue cotton with a narrow white stripe. It was sleeveless, with a narrow white lace frill at the neck and shoulder-line. It was mercifully of creaseless material, and while not exactly as good as new, at least it was an improvement on the crushed jeans and blouse she was wearing.

She put her head round the door. Piran was sitting on the sofa, with Jules beside him, an open book on the boy's knee, and he was chatting away quite freely to his uncle. Relieved, Polly called across the room, 'Can you wait while I have a shower—if I can get it to work?'

Piran looked up and grinned. 'Certainly—take your time. If you need help, call me.' His attention returned to Jules.

In the bathroom, Polly stripped off and studied the taps on the shower. The water might not be hot, but she would brave a cold shower for the luxury of feeling clean again. The set-up was different from the shower at her hotel, but eventually she managed to get the water running out feebly. True enough, it was cold. Bracing herself, she stepped beneath the trickle and, gasping, began to rub herself down briskly.

It happened with terrifying suddenness. One minute the water was sprinkling down in separate icy droplets. The next minute the whole contraption gave a convulsive gurgle and gushed down steaming hot water on Polly's head. She let out a wild yelp, slithered backwards, and finished in a heap at the far end of the bath.

Behind her the door crashed open and then she was being lifted bodily out of the bath and Piran's horrified voice was shouting, 'Polly! What happened? Are you hurt? Good God, the water's nearly boiling! Have you scalded yourself—let me see.'

His hands were on her body, supporting her, but

she was beyond caring. 'I—it was—running cold—and then—suddenly—it went hot.' Her teeth were chattering with shock.

'You stupid child, of course it went hot—you had the hot tap turned on.' He reached out and turned it off.

His anger brought her back to reality and she was suddenly aware that she was completely naked and his hands were on her, tingling on her bare flesh. Her stomach flipped over and she wriggled out of his grasp and made a grab for a pink towel that hung limply across the end of the bath, pulling it hastily round herself. 'I'm not hurt,' she muttered.

She was aware that he was chuckling. 'O.K., so you're not hurt, if you were you wouldn't be worrying about displaying your very charming body. Just think how Eve must have felt in the garden of Eden when she found she was naked. I'm sure Adam didn't object.'

He leaned against the door, surveying her with amused dark eyes. 'Do you still want to take a shower, or would you like to get dressed and then we'll be on our way?'

She gathered the towel closer round her, but it was much too small to cover all of her and she was burningly aware of Piran's eyes passing down to rest appreciatively on her pink breasts, still damp from the hot water.

Suddenly his mood seemed to change. 'O.K. then, get dressed,' he said shortly. 'I'll be out for a while—perhaps you'll be ready when I get back?'

'I'll be ready,' she said, rather crestfallen now. 'I—I'm sorry,' she added in a small voice. 'I seem to be causing you a lot of trouble, one way and another.'

He was halfway out of the bathroom, his back towards her. 'You can say that again. Now, hurry up.'

She heard Jules's voice raised questioningly in the living room, and his uncle's replying reassuringly. Then the outer door of the apartment closed with a snap, and Polly crept hastily across the little lobby and into the bedroom, where she sank on to the bed that had caused all the trouble last night, and tried to get her composure back. But all she could think of was the disturbing sensation of the man's arms round her body, the touch of his hard fingers on her bare flesh. She shivered. What had happened to her? She hadn't fallen in love with him and never would. He wasn't her kind of man at all. She had always preferred the fair, easy-going boys at college to the dark- sexy ones, who always seemed to be issuing a challenge of some sort that she didn't care to meet.

She supposed she was just totally inexperienced, and this first encounter with a sexually disturbing male had taken her by surprise. But nothing could come of their relationship, so the sooner she got a grip on herself the better!

Having come to this sensible decision she proceeded to put on the blue dress and pay particular attention to her face, which was still flushed from the agitation of the last few minutes. After she had smoothed on a paler shade of foundation, she leaned towards the mirror, carefully applying eye-shadow. It was a sapphire blue, two or three shades darker than her eyes, and she hadn't used it before because she simply hadn't bothered with make-up for her days sightseeing alone in Paris. But now she was glad she had bought it, and the effect pleased her. It made her look older, less childish. She towelled her damp hair and brushed it behind her ears; that made her look older too. At last, tolerably pleased with her appearance, she went back to the living room. If she were going to play-act the part of Piran St Just's fiancée for the next few days, she was determined to look the part as far as possible.

Jules was curled up on the sofa, his dark head lowered over a heavy book, supported on his knees. He raised his eyes as he saw Polly. Then he said in his serious, unchildlike way, 'You look pretty, *mademoiselle*.'

'Thank you, Jules,' Polly laughed, 'what a very nice compliment.' She sat down beside him and looked over his shoulder at the book he was reading.

'*Dinosaurs in Ancient Britain*. Aren't they huge—look at that one!' She pointed to a picture of a wondrous beast prowling the forests of the past.

Jules's dark eyes were shining. 'How big is he? As big as this room?'

'Oh much, much bigger than this room.'

'As big as the apartment?'

'Bigger than that. Almost as big as the whole building, I'd say. There's a fossil skeleton of one in a museum in London. I'm sure your uncle would take you to see it if you asked him.'

'Would he?' Jules sounded doubtful. Obviously he couldn't rely on treats like that since his father died. 'But we can see the footprints in—where is Uncle Piran's house?'

'In Dorset, by the sea.'

'And we can see them there? He said we could.'

'Yes, I expect so,' said Polly. Jules was obviously still relying upon her being there, but she didn't want to let him bank too heavily upon that happening.

'You're *sure* so,' he insisted. 'When you marry Uncle Piran you'll live in his house, won't you, Mademoiselle Polly?'

Polly passed her tongue over dry lips, trying to think of a reply that wouldn't be a complete lie.

Then, 'Of course she will.' Piran's voice came from

the doorway behind them and their two heads turned abruptly as he walked across the room. 'Of course she will, won't you, *ma chérie*?'

He lowered himself on to the sofa beside her and put his arm round her waist and planted a kiss just behind her ear. Polly's heart began to race and she drew away a little, but he pulled her back, laughing. He was obviously in high good humour.

'Now then, you two, are you ready at last? We'll go shopping, then. I've got a taxi waiting outside, I thought the car would be a bit of an encumbrance in the centre of Paris. Come along, it's a beautiful day.'

It was indeed a beautiful day. It must have rained in the night, for the streets had a washed look that shone silver in the sunlight. Polly had brought a white woollen jacket, but she didn't need it. When they stepped out of the taxi the sun shone warm on her bare arms and the air was soft and fragrant with the scents that drifted along the boulevard from the massed flower stalls outside the Madeleine.

Already, in the five days she had spent there, Polly had grown to love Paris: its wide, tree-lined streets packed and jammed with cars, its elegant, fascinating shops, and perhaps most of all the cafés with their tables set out on the pavement under striped awnings. They stopped at one of these cafés now, and took the only unoccupied table. Piran ordered coffee for himself and Polly and a fabulous ice-cream for Jules, who was beginning to look more relaxed and happy than at any moment since Polly had first set eyes on him in the coach.

'We'll make for the Boulevard Haussmann,' Piran announced, as they left the café. 'I know of a shop there where we might buy you a ring, and afterwards there is the Galeries Lafayette, where you can get fitted out with anything you need in the way of clothes

and things.' He didn't wait for her consent, he set out
along the wide, crowded pavements at a brisk pace,
weaving his way between the more leisurely strollers
who proclaimed themselves Parisians by the very fact
of their absence of urgency. Polly took Jules's hand
and they had almost to run to keep up with him. He
did, however, stop when he arrived at a road crossing,
and shepherded them across with the greatest of
courtesy. He was, Polly thought once more, a
curiously double-sided character.

The shop where he proposed to buy the ring was
not at all the glittering emporium that Polly had
expected to find in Paris. It was small and dark,
tucked away in a narrow side street, and was obviously
more an antique dealer's than a jeweller's. The man
who emerged from a back room as they went in was
small and elderly, with old-fashioned pince-nez
spectacles perched on the end of a beaky nose, and a
wide, clever forehead. Piran greeted him by his
name—Monsieur Jacabo—and his face broke into a
beam of pleasure and recognition. A conversation
followed between the two men in a stream of rapid
French that Polly could make very little sense of.

Then Piran drew her forward. '*Puis-je vous presenter
ma fiancée, Mademoiselle West, monsieur?*' he said
formally, and Polly found her hand grasped in
Monsieur Jacabo's dry fingers, while he expressed
himself delighted to make her acquaintance. Jules,
also, was introduced, and then they all repaired to a
tiny room at the back of the shop, where Monsieur
Jacabo produced several boxes with velvet linings, in
which were lovingly arranged a selection of the most
beautiful antique jewellery that Polly had ever seen.
None of the rings, Monsieur Jacabo explained, was
less than a hundred years old, and some of them
considerably more.

Piran smiled lovingly at her and pushed a box towards her. 'One of these, perhaps, *mon amour*?'

It was absurd, she thought crossly, there was absolutely no need for all this play-acting. Surely they could have gone to some inexpensive jeweller's and bought a ring—even an imitation stone would have filled the bill. It was only to be hers for a few days and she wasn't likely to be meeting anybody who could tell the difference.

But Piran evidently wanted it done this way, so she might as well choose something which it would be a pleasure to wear—even temporarily. She touched one ring gently. It was a poem of small sapphires and diamonds in a delicate scroll setting that enhanced the beauty of the stones. 'That's really lovely,' she said, and Piran nodded agreement. 'Let's see if it fits.'

He picked up her left hand and slipped the ring on her fingers, and Polly felt the blood rush to her cheeks. She couldn't meet his eyes but fixed her gaze upon her finger, where the ring fitted perfectly. 'A good choice,' Piran said quietly, and went on holding her hand in his for a few more moments before he let it go and proceeded to the business side of the deal with Monsieur Jacabo. A few minutes later they left the shop, followed by the elderly man's good wishes.

The Galeries Lafayette was very like any large department store in London, only perhaps a little more exotic. Piran and Jules accompanied Polly to the gown department, where a *vendeuse* appeared immediately, smilingly obliging and interested. Polly noticed how many sidelong glances were cast in Piran's direction and wondered with amusement whether she would have been as well served if she had arrived alone, in her modest chain-store dress.

'I feel like Cinderella before the ball,' she whispered to Jules, perched on a slim, gold chair.

'I know that story,' he said importantly. 'Cind'rella married the prince and they lived happily ever after.'

Polly couldn't resist glancing at Piran as he murmured, 'A fairy story, of course,' his dark eyes mocking.

Polly would normally have lingered over her choice of clothes. She was so accustomed to looking at the price-tag on everything before she even tried it on that what seemed to her Piran's reckless extravagance put her head in a whirl. His approach to anything that he liked seemed to be, 'That suits you very well—we'll have it.'

'You're spending far too much money,' she hissed at him as the *vendeuse* approached again with an armful of gossamer evening dresses. 'And I'm not likely to need one of *those* anyway.' But she couldn't help a longing glance towards the lovely, floating things of chiffon and lace and silk in their subtle colours.

'Oh, you never know,' he replied airily. 'I just might decide to take you out to the Opéra one evening.' He glanced towards Jules. 'Would you let me take Mademoiselle Polly out, Jules? If I asked Madame Arnot to keep an eye on you?' He added as an aside to Polly. 'Madame Arnot is the *concierge*—a good soul.'

'Of course I would not mind,' Jules replied in a very dignified, grown-up voice. 'I often have stayed alone, you understand.'

'Yes,' his uncle said. His mouth was grim although his voice remained gentle. 'I understand, Jules. I understand very well.'

Within an hour their shopping was completed. Polly couldn't remember all that had been bought, but it included a lightweight sand-coloured safari suit for travelling, a woollen suit in a misty blue for colder days when they got back to England, a couple of pairs of stylish pants (no more jeans!) and a selection of tops. Most exciting of all, a gorgeous evening gown of white, flowing net, with a deep gathered froth of lace outlining the low-cut oval neckline. Piran chose it, as he chose all the other clothes, regarding each item critically as she emerged from the fitting room. It was certainly not the first time he had bought clothes for a girl, although his motives on this occasion might be rather exceptional.

After a while Polly stopped protesting about the amount of money he was spending, which seemed to her totally unnecessary. After all, she told herself, he could no doubt afford to amuse himself in this way. He certainly gave the impression of being rich.

As they were on their way out of the store, having made arrangements for their purchases to be delivered to the apartment, she found out the reason for her impression. They were passing through the book department and Jules hung back, his small face eager as his eyes passed over the rows and rows of books.

Polly put a hand on Piran's arm. 'Do stop and let him browse for a bit,' she pleaded. 'Books are his thing, you know. I've found out that about him already.'

For some reason Piran didn't look too pleased. He turned his back on the two of them and retired to the far corner of the department, where he appeared to be engaged in searching for some particular book. Polly stayed with Jules, amused at the rapt expression on his face as he pored over the display on the stand, most of which must have been far beyond his comprehension. Her own eyes wandered over the paperbacks. She would buy something popular, she thought, which would make easy reading and help to improve her French.

Then her eye caught an island-stand in the centre of the department, each shelf displaying the same paperback. The cover picture was of a great black bird with spread wings and claws extended. Rather frightening, Polly thought, not her sort of light reading at all. But something about the book made her go closer to see the title.

She read: *Le Grand Corbeau*. And scrawled below, blackly, the signature, *Piran St Just*.

Polly's heart gave an odd lurch. Of course—that was why his name had been vaguely familiar to her from the beginning! Piran St Just, best-selling author, whose thrillers and suspense stories seemed always to be among the top ten. She glanced over at his back. She had an idea that he, too, had seen the stand and hoped that neither she nor Jules would notice it. She walked over and stood beside him.

'*Le Grand Corbeau*,' she said thoughtfully, slanting a glance up at him. 'Does that translate as *The Raven*?'

'Oh, you've seen it, have you?' he growled out of the side of his mouth, peering back over his shoulder as if he were a character in one of his own spy stories. 'Well, don't mention it to my nephew; he probably wouldn't approve of my style in fiction. And anyway, he's too young. My books are definitely for adults only.'

'Very interesting!' Polly murmured, her eyes dancing. She walked away and collected Jules, who was clutching one slim volume on stained glass windows. He looked up at Polly, his eyes huge. 'Do you think *mon oncle* would buy it for me?' he asked in a small, timid voice.

'Oh, I should think so. Let's go and ask him.'

Piran turned as they approached, a wary expression on his face. Polly said with a grin, 'Jules has excellent taste in literature, it seems. He wonders if he might have this book?'

Piran paid for it hastily and hustled them both out

of the shop. 'Are we going back to the apartment for lunch? Jules and I are getting hungry,' Polly enquired as they stepped into the sunshine again.

Piran suggested they should find a likely-looking restaurant for lunch and then do some sightseeing afterwards. 'I thought we might try the Pompidou Centre. If young Jules is going to be an architect he should see some really modern stuff as well as the ancient buildings.'

Polly passed the afternoon in a delicious haze. The Pompidou Centre, or Beaubourg, as the Parisians affectionately called it, was the most extraordinary building she had ever seen. Everything that is normally concealed inside a building was here frankly displayed on the outside. And not only displayed but emphasised in bright colours. Piran took them first to the east side, where enormous pipes rose vertically from bottom to top, coloured according to their uses— green for water, yellow for electricity and blue for air-conditioning, with here and there bright red slabs that were part of the lift shafts.

Jules stared, fascinated, while his uncle explained how President Pompidou had decided to build a Centre for the arts of the present time, and how a great competition was arranged, in which hundreds of architects from many different countries took part.

On the opposite side of the building a glass tunnel rose across the outside like a giant caterpillar, and inside this was the main escalator.

They entered the building and came into an enormous open space on the ground floor, that Piran called the Forum. Jules would have lingered round the bookstalls, but Piran guided them towards the entrance to the escalator. 'Come along, Jules,' he urged. 'We'll go up to the top and look over the roofs of Paris. Don't be frightened, it's quite safe.'

Jules threw back his head and stuck out his small chin. 'I'm not frightened,' he said stoutly.

'I expect I shall be,' Polly laughed. 'I don't much care for heights.'

But in the end she was too entranced to be alarmed as the escalator took them upwards inside its glass tube, and at each landing (giving access to the different floors inside the building) they could pause and savour the incredible view spread out below, the buildings appearing smaller and smaller as they neared the top.

Here they remained, looking down across Paris, and at the square immediately below, where all sorts of sideshows seemed to be taking place, each one surrounded by its own little group of spectators.

Inside the building again they made their way through galleries and museums. Polly was inclined to quicken her steps now, as she saw Jules looking more and more weary, but determined not to show it. He would have stayed for hours in the special children's library, but she whispered to Piran, 'I think we should get him away now, he's had enough excitement for one day.'

He nodded, grinning. 'I'm sure you're right, Nanny,' he said, and Polly pulled a face at him, telling herself to take the name in good part. But all the way back to the apartment in the taxi she found herself wishing that somehow she could be more than just a temporary nanny to Jules, and a—a—what was she to Piran? Just a very ordinary girl who happened, at the moment, to be useful to him. Keep remembering that, Polly, and don't get ideas in your mind above your station, she told herself, with a wry attempt at humour.

They arrived home as the light was fading, tired and happy. Like a family party after a successful outing,

Polly thought with a little pang as she slumped down
and kicked off her pumps.

'Ooh, that was hard on the feet,' she sighed. 'But
what a fabulous place! It was fun, I enjoyed it so
much.'

Piran had bought wine while they were out. He
stood now with a bottle in one hand and a corkscrew
in the other, looking down at her with an odd
expression on his face. 'Your eyes are shining like
diamonds,' he said softly. And then spoilt it by
adding, 'You look like a little girl who's been given a
treat.'

'It *was* a treat,' she said. 'But I'm not a little girl.'

His only response to that was a wry lift of the
eyebrow. Then he put a glass in her hand. 'Try this, I
think you'll like it.'

Wretched man! Polly fumed to herself as she
prepared a meal. Nothing would persuade him to take
her seriously.

But at least he noticed the work she had put in this
morning. As they sat at table he looked around with an
appreciative eye. 'You've managed to freshen up this
place considerably,' he said. 'It looks almost like a
home. Flowers on the table, even.' He sniffed the
yellow button chrysanthemums that Polly had bought
at the market this morning.

'Jules helped a lot,' Polly said. 'We really cleaned
out the kitchen between us, didn't we, Jules?'

The boy's dark eyes were bright. 'I scrubbed the
sink,' he piped up, and Piran complimented him
gravely.

Afterwards Polly made coffee and warmed milk for
Jules and they all sat around and looked at Jules's
book and Piran promised to take him to see some
stained glass windows next day.

'The boy really hasn't been anywhere or seen

anything, apparently,' he said in disgust to Polly, when Jules had been tucked up in bed. 'He was too young when Maurice was alive—anyway, he hardly remembers his father. It amazes me how good his English is. It's almost as if he *wants* to remember.' They were in the kitchen and he was leaning against the door-post watching Polly wash up the supper things. As he spoke he took a dish out of her hands and dried it vigorously. Perhaps not so chauvinist after all! Polly liked a man who would help with the washing-up.

'But all that is going to change,' he mused on, piling up plates as he dried them. 'He's got a good mind and he's going to be given every opportunity to use it.'

Polly put the last plate on the draining board and wrung out the dishcloth. She turned and looked at him. 'You'd do anything to get Jules into your care, wouldn't you? Anything at all?'

He nodded and she thought she had never seen such determination in anyone's face before. 'Anything at all,' he said.

Polly was to remember that in the days that lay ahead.

CHAPTER FIVE

THAT night Polly slept in the second bed in Jules's room. This morning she had hung the wet mattress over a chair beside the open window and it had dried in the sun. A good deal of searching had disclosed some clean sheets, and she now had her nightdress and toilet things, and felt much more civilised.

To her relief Jules slept through the night, with no return of his asthma, and Polly herself slept soundly too and wakened to see the sun stealing between the curtains. Jules was still fast asleep and she threw her nylon wrap round her and tiptoed across the lobby to the bathroom. The room that Piran was sleeping in led off the big living-room, but no sound came from either direction. This time she was very careful with the controls and managed to take a cool, refreshing shower. Back in the bedroom she dressed quickly in the blue cotton dress. She brushed her hair carefully but put no make-up on. It was no use trying to persuade herself that Piran would notice what she looked like, she told herself severely. She was a young girl who was useful to him at the moment, and that was the extent of his interest in her. Everything he had done, even buying the lovely ring and all those clothes (which would be delivered today, she supposed) was merely part of his plan to get Jules for himself. But she couldn't help feeling a little surge of excitement at the prospect of the day ahead.

In the living-room she pulled back the velvet curtains and stole a glance across at Piran's room. The door was open wide and through it she saw the bed just as she had tidied it up yesterday morning. A closer look showed her that the room was empty. There was only one conclusion to draw. Piran hadn't slept in the apartment last night.

Polly's mind raced. Why hadn't he told her he wouldn't be here? If he expected her to account to him for her movements, then surely he should do the same?

She put the cloth on the table and slammed down the plates. Presumably the wretched man would have the decency to return for breakfast. Her anger increased while she was making toast and getting out eggs for omelettes, and came to boiling point as time went on and he hadn't put in an appearance. Where, she couldn't help asking herself, had he spent the night? And with whom? The obvious answer occurred to her at once, and the picture that presented itself of Piran being entertained by some silky, sophisticated *fille de joie* in a perfumed Paris apartment scattered with satin cushions and littered with wine bottles and empty glasses gave her a sick feeling inside. Of course, she argued with herself, trying to blot out the picture, he might have friends in Paris, but if he had intended to stay with friends why on earth couldn't he have said so? Possibilities flitted round her head like nagging insects as she went on preparing the breakfast.

Jules wakened and got himself washed and dressed—he was a very self-sufficient little boy for his age. He came into the kitchen and stood beside the table. 'I'm hungry,' he proclaimed. 'When can we eat?'

'Not long now,' Polly told him. 'Your Uncle Piran has just gone out for a few minutes, but as soon as he comes back I'll make the omelettes.'

'Do we have to wait for him? Couldn't I have my omelette now?'

Polly clapped her hands together. 'You're right,' she said rather loudly, 'why should we wait for him? We will have breakfast together, Jules, you and I.' And as the butter began to sizzle in the omelette pan she felt she had struck a tiny blow for feminine independence.

They finished breakfast and Jules retired to his room with his new book. Polly was clearing the table when Piran walked in, looking his brigand self and badly in need of a shave.

He stared at the empty table. 'Sorry,' he yawned. 'I overslept—am I late?'

Polly's anger had by this time given way to anxiety. For the last half-hour horrid possibilities had been suggesting themselves. Piran had gone out for cigarettes or a paper or something. He had been mugged. He had been run over. Seeing him suddenly now, unhurt, gave her a churning in the pit of her stomach and she ran to him. 'Oh, I'm so glad you've come!' she babbled. 'I thought—I thought——' She clutched his arm as if to satisfy herself that he was real.

'Hey—steady on!' He held her a little way away, studying her face quizzically. 'What's wrong?'

She pulled herself together immediately and stepped back, and his casual manner made her anger boil over again. Her eyes flashed blue fire at him. 'Why couldn't you have told me you were going to be away all night? I didn't know what had happened. I thought you might have been run over or injured or something. I think it was most—most inconsiderate of you!' She turned her back on him and walked across to the table. 'Do you want any breakfast?' she enquired shortly. 'Or have you already had some at—wherever you've been?'

He was grinning widely as he joined her at the table. 'I should very much like some breakfast, Polly. If it isn't too much trouble, that is,' he added with mock humility. 'And I apologise sincerely for causing you any worry.' He sat down and stretched out his legs. 'I assure you I had every intention of occupying Madame Brunet's room again last night. The fact was that I went downstairs for a breath of air before turning in, and encountered our worthy *concierge*, who offered me a room in her own flat which she lets to the occasional visitor. She seemed to take it for granted that it wouldn't be seemly for you and me to share the apartment here, unchaperoned.' He chuckled. 'Contrary to our British belief, your French housewife has a very proper judgment of what is "done" and what is not "done". So, wishing to keep in her good books, I accepted gratefully.' He chuckled again. 'I can't tell you how pleased she was. You seem to have made quite an impression on her in a short time. I imagine she thought she was rescuing you from a fate worse than death.'

'I'm much obliged to her,' Polly said stiffly. 'Now, if you'd like to go and shave I'll cook you some breakfast.'

She turned away, but he caught her by the wrist and spun her round. 'Ah, don't be like that, Polly. We're partners, remember? And in case what I've just said has put ideas into your head, let me tell you that I wouldn't dream of trying to take advantage of the situation and make love to you if you didn't want it, you must know that.' His dark eyes creased at the corners. 'Which is not to say I wouldn't like to. Very much.'

She started to say, 'I don't know what you're talking about. I——' But her eyes were drawn to his smiling eyes, and the look between them held and lengthened. Polly's heart seemed to stop beating and then began again with heavy, suffocating strokes. She waited, hardly breathing, for what she knew was going to happen.

'*Very* much,' he repeated softly, and pulled her against him. 'You're very sweet, Polly.' Slowly his mouth came down on hers, and Polly was lost in a breathtaking turmoil of feeling. Her anger, her anxiety, all got caught up in a response that she was hardly conscious of making. His kiss had started undemandingly, but as her hands went up round his neck, seemingly of their own accord, his lips stiffened and then relaxed against hers, parting her own lips, moving against them, until she spun dizzily in an ecstasy of pure feeling. Her fingers clung to his rough, springy hair, and moved down to encounter into the warm nape of his neck, as his unshaved chin scratched against her soft flesh.

'You're so sweet,' he muttered again, and his hands dropped to her waist, pressing her against the taut hardness of his body. Wave upon wave of pleasure washed over her. She was transported to a world of sensual arousal that she had only heard about but never experienced. She let out a little moan and her fingers dug themselves convulsively into the hollow of his neck, as she returned his kisses hungrily. Then a sudden sound from behind made her wrench her mouth away from Piran's. Jules was standing in the doorway of his room, a wide grin on his face.

Piran's arms disengaged themselves immediately. He took a couple of strides and lifted the boy up, holding him high in the air. 'You old ruffian, what do you mean by playing gooseberry?'

Jules looked startled and then, as he caught his uncle's smile, he smiled back, still a little timidly. 'What is gooseberry?' he enquired, and Piran ruffled his dark hair and said, 'I'll tell you one day—now, come and watch me shave while Mademoiselle Polly

makes me some breakfast, which she has been kind
enough to offer to do.' There was a wicked gleam in
his eyes as they met Polly's. Then he turned back to
Jules. 'And don't you think you'd better practise
calling her Aunt Polly, Jules? It sounds more friendly,
doesn't it?'

Jules surveyed them both in his serious way. 'Yes,'
he said, 'I think I should like that.'

Somehow Polly managed to produce a reasonably
light omelette and fresh toast and coffee, in spite of the
fact that her hands were unsteady and her throat was
aching with tension. What on earth had possessed her
to respond like that to what was simply intended to be
a casual kiss? She must be on her guard and not let it
happen again.

It took all her courage to return to the living room
and serve Piran's breakfast to him, looking as if
nothing of particular importance had happened. She
had to keep reminding herself that to a man like Piran
a kiss was just a kiss, however it might have lit a fuse
inside her that promised to go on burning.

'Thanks, Polly, this is super.' He tucked into his
breakfast with zest. 'Join me in another cup of coffee,
won't you, and we can discuss the day's programme. I
have to see my friend at the Embassy this morning,
but I'll come back for lunch—and mind you're here
this time,' he added darkly.

Polly spent the morning cleaning the bedroom that
she was sharing with Jules, which took a considerable
time as Jules kept interrupting her work with pleas to
look at some picture or other in a book, or interpret a
sentence. But at last the job was finished and she was
able to turn her attention to the other bedroom. She
stood looking around. This was where Piran should
have slept last night, but hadn't. He had had a very
ready explanation, but could she believe it?

She sighed. What did it matter whether she believed him or not? She would only be in his company until he got Jules back to England, and after that her usefulness would come to an end.

Just make the most of your extended holiday, Polly, she advised herself, and don't start getting any romantic ideas about falling in love.

There was a knock at the door and it was the *concierge*, her plump face beaming, the bun of dark hair perched jauntily on top of her head. '*Bonjour, mademoiselle.* I come to enquire if there is any small matter with which I can help you.'

'You are very kind.' Polly marshalled her French. 'Please come in.'

The woman entered the living room and stood looking around her with unconcealed surprise. 'You have performed a miracle, *mademoiselle*. Never have I seen this room so clean and tidy.' She sketched a gesture of amazement. 'Madame Brunet——!' An expressive shrug.

Jules came into the room to see what was going on and the *concierge* patted his head amiably. 'You have your uncle now to look after you, *mon petit*, that is good, *n'est-ce pas?*'

Jules hesitated, his small face screwed up as he pondered the question. Then he said firmly, '*Oui, madame*, that is good. And I also have Tante Polly. That is good also.' He moved nearer to Polly and grinned up confidently at her.

The *concierge* surveyed them both benevolently. 'You have a good man there, *mademoiselle*, an excellent man. When he approach me last evening with a request that I should find him a separate room, I tell myself, "Ah, there goes one man who knows what is right."' She nodded her dark head up and down approvingly. 'I wish you every happiness in your marriage, *mademoiselle*.'

Polly thanked her and eventually managed to end the interview, with the *concierge* still talking away as she trundled off down the stairs.

Polly walked thoughtfully back into the apartment. So—it was Piran who had looked for a separate room, so that he would not have to share the apartment with her overnight. Why? Was it because the bedroom hadn't been cleaned, or—and this seemed much more likely—that he didn't want to get involved in any way with her? Had he guessed how violently she was attracted to him and not wanted to risk sharing the apartment with her overnight? Her cheeks burned as she remembered how she had clung to him when he came back this morning, how passionately she had responded to what he intended to be no more than a casual kiss. He must think she was trying to set some sort of trap for him. Shame and humiliation scalded through her and she sank into a chair as her knees refused to support her. It wouldn't happen again, she vowed, she would be so cool and collected that he couldn't possibly know how she was feeling inside. All the more reason, she assured herself, for saying goodbye as soon as they arrived back in England tomorrow.

By the time Piran came in, soon after midday, Polly had managed to get a grip on herself and was able to greet him coolly and pleasantly. 'How did the interview go?' she enquired.

'Swimmingly,' he announced. 'Fortunately I have a copy of Jules's birth certificate and as he was born in England he's a British subject. So—no problems, he can travel on my passport. Just a bit of paper-work to get through, that's all, then we can fly back to London. I've booked our flight for the day after

tomorrow. We shan't need the car I've got on hire any
longer. I'll return it this afternoon and we can get
around by taxi or take the Metro. That suit you?'

'Yes, of course,' Polly said briskly. A day and a half
and then it would be over, and she could start learning
to forget Piran St Just. She glanced at him and away
again as she added, 'What a pity you bought all those
clothes for me. They were delivered a short time ago.
Perhaps the shop would take them back again, as they
haven't been worn?'

'Rubbish,' Piran said crisply. 'They're a small
enough recompense for all you've done for me, and I
hope you'll accept them in that spirit. Meanwhile,
suppose you put on one of those pretty dresses and I'll
take you both out to lunch at a funny little restaurant I
know in Montmartre, and then we'll do some
sightseeing.'

All that day and the next Paris was pure magic.
Piran's mood was one of happy companionship, and
Polly was able to put her earlier discomfort behind her
and enjoy herself for the short time that remained.
Piran was a wonderful guide and even the places Polly
had seen earlier came to new, fascinating life in his
company. He bought her films for her camera and she
snapped everything: the pavement artists of
Montmartre; the spurting fountains of the Palais de
Chaillot with the Eiffel Tower in the background;
Notre Dame Cathedral from the river, when they went
on a pleasure-boat cruise; the crowded pavement cafés
with their striped awnings; the elegant shops in the
Rue du Faubourg St Honoré with their famous names
and exotic window-displays; the Champs Elysées and
the Arc de Triomphe.

'I'm not being very original, I'm afraid,' she
admitted, as they strolled under the trees in the park,
on their last afternoon. 'I just want to remember

everything—all the famous sights that seem to be the essence of Paris. Then I can browse through my album on horrid wet evenings in London, at the end of a day's work, and remember it all.'

Piran tucked his hand through her arm. 'Remember me too, perhaps?'

'Oh, of course.' Polly's eyes danced with mischief. 'Jules—and you.'

On her other side, Jules tugged at her arm. 'Please, can we see some stained glass windows now?' he pleaded. 'Just before we go home?'

Piran clapped a hand to his brow. 'Goodness me, I quite forgot! There are some windows that are a must. Come along, both of you.'

Polly looked doubtfully at Jules. His short legs must be very tired, she thought; they had done a good deal of walking on this last day. 'Is it far?' she asked Piran, but he said, 'Very near—just over the bridge to the Cité.'

They passed over the bridge and soon through a courtyard and along a vaulted passage. 'Where are we going, Uncle Piran?' Jules whispered the words excitedly.

'La Sainte Chapelle, my lad. Your uncle's favourite place in Paris.' Piran spoke lightly, but Polly thought she detected an undertone of gravity in his voice. They entered a darkish building with a low roof and Piran led the way up a spiral staircase. Jules climbed manfully after him and Polly brought up the rear. As she reached the top step she drew in a breath of sheer wonder. Up and up, until she had to strain her neck back to see the top, soared the most exquisite stained glass windows she had ever seen. The immensely tall, narrow panes glowed with an unearthly light, red and blue and gold, and the thin leaden dividing bars carved them into smaller shapes, so that they resembled long, glittering necklaces hanging from the vaulted ceiling above. 'Oh, it's so beautiful!' Polly breathed. She glanced at Piran, who was standing staring straight ahead of him, his face grim.

As she spoke he relaxed and in the semi-gloom the smile he gave her made her heart lift suddenly. 'Maurice and I used to roam about Paris in the old days,' he said softly. 'When we found this place it knocked us sideways.' He was silent for a moment or two and then he added, 'I've never been back since. I've never brought anyone here before. Somehow it seems right that Jules should see it.'

He wasn't all tough, Polly thought. There was a sensitive side to him as well, if you could reach it. She blinked, suddenly touched by the thought of the two young men, long ago, finding this jewelled casket of a place and loving it.

He was leaning down to Jules. 'Here you have really daring architecture, my boy. It's not only the architect of Beaubourg who has fantastic new ideas. Six hundred years ago they had new ideas too. Look, the ceiling is supported only on those thin columns of stone, while the walls between are made of stained glass. The architect must have been playing a joke on someone, don't you think? Usually windows are put into walls, but here the walls are put into the windows. Clever, isn't it?'

Jules giggled with delight, and he was still giggling as they made their way back into the sunlight. Polly's eyes met Piran's over the boy's head and an unspoken message passed between them. Jules was already becoming a happy little boy.

That evening, when he was in bed, and Polly and Piran were lingering over their coffee after supper, Piran said with satisfaction, 'We've made good start with Jules. Already he's glad to be with us and trusting us. When we get back home I want to see him become a real little boy. Books are fine, but it'll be great to see him running about on the heath with Judy—she's my Labrador—or riding a bicycle. I must buy him a bicycle,' he added, his dark eyes thoughtful. 'All little boys ought to have bicycles.' And Polly knew that he was again reliving his own boyhood.

With a pang, she thrust aside the picture that Piran's words had conjured up. She said practically, 'What time does our flight arrive in London tomorrow?'

He raised dark brows lazily. 'I don't know exactly. Why? Does it matter?'

'It does matter rather to me,' she said. 'I need to book a room for the night, until I can find something permanent. I gave up my share in a flat before I came to Paris. Oh, and I have to go back there to collect the rest of my belongings.' She had decided that their arrival in London should be the end of the road for her involvement. It would be a wrench to leave Jules, but it would be better for him in the long run not to be too dependent on her, and the longer she stayed with him the more he would rely on her. When she wasn't there any longer he would naturally turn to his uncle.

Piran's dark eyes glittered under their heavy lids. 'You're very anxious to get away from us, aren't you, Polly?'

'I have to make plans,' she said.

He sat back in his chair, studying her face. 'For your future?'

'What else?' she said impatiently. She resented being quizzed, and now this episode was coming to an end she had a strong wish to finish the whole matter and start trying to forget Jules and Piran St Just and get her life into some sort of order.

'And have you given any thought to what those plans might be?' he went on probing.

'I haven't had much time recently, have I?' Polly said flatly, and he burst out laughing.

'No, I'm afraid we have rather dragged you into our affairs, Jules and I. Are you so very anxious to get away from us?' he repeated.

She could no longer avoid the fact that there was a meaning behind his questions. She sat straight in the corner of the sofa and put down her coffee cup. 'Are you offering me a job, Mr St Just?'

'Piran,' he said patiently.

'All right—Piran. Are you offering me a job?'

'Are you looking for a job?' Oh heavens, why couldn't he come to the point?

'Of course I am. I can't afford to be out of work for long. And I don't fancy queueing up at the Social Security office, although it may come to that. Teaching jobs are not easy to come by—especially when you haven't had any experience.'

He studied her face in silence; then his gaze moved down over her slender form in its pretty white dress with the neat blue patterning—one of the new dresses he had bought for her. 'I don't think you're cut out for teaching,' he said. 'Certainly not in a big school.'

'Why not?' The blue eyes flashed indignantly. 'I managed my teaching practice quite well.' That wasn't quite true; she remembered her positive terror when she first faced a class of fourteen-year-olds, remembered how she had wept each night in bed at the thought of facing them again the next day. And it hadn't got much better as the time went on.

'I just don't think you're tough enough,' said Piran St Just simply, and it was all the more maddening because she had a horrid suspicion that he was right.

'Well, I'll just have to do my best,' she said shortly.

'You don't have to. That was what I was trying—

rather clumsily, I'm afraid—to lead up to. I can offer you a job. And it will involve a certain amount of teaching, of a sort, if you're really so keen on teaching.'

Polly waited, her thoughts performing somersaults. He was going to ask her to continue to look after Jules, of course, and that would be lovely. There was nothing she would like more. But—but it would mean seeing more of Piran St Just, wouldn't it? Prudence told her that would be dangerous—worse than dangerous—fatal. She could so easily make a fool of herself over the man—any girl could. He had everything: he was handsome, dynamic, charming when he wanted to be. And sexy—oh yes, that too. So far he'd been careful not to alarm her, because they were in this funny sort of situation together and he didn't dare to risk frightening her away. But she got the feeling that he wouldn't always be so careful. She still shivered inside when she remembered how he had kissed her yesterday—and that had been her doing too, she had all but asked him to.

Yes, she thought, she could so easily fall in love with him; she was half in love with him already. It would be asking for heartache to involve herself in his life any longer.

'Aren't you going to ask me what the job is?' His eyes were smiling under the heavy lids.

'I think I can guess,' she said. 'To go on looking after Jules for a while?'

'There's more to it than that, Polly.' He got out of his chair and came and sat beside her on the sofa, not very close, but close enough to start her heart beating uncomfortably. 'May I ask you some questions?' he said.

She shrugged. 'I'm sure you will, whether I agree or not.'

'Quite,' he said imperturbably. 'You don't have to answer, of course, but it would make things easier if you could bring yourself to do so. First—you're alone, aren't you, Polly?'

'What do you mean—alone?' she asked, startled.

'I mean, you haven't got anyone to turn to? If you need anything, or if you're in trouble of any kind?'

'I don't see what it's got to do with you, Mr St Just.'

'Piran—please. We're not strangers any more.' He was very serious now, not challenging, or ironic, or teasing. 'Polly, I know we've only known each other a couple of days. In effect I'm a stranger to you, but can you believe that I've been telling you the truth, as I know it?'

He was so bland, so reasonable, but could she trust him entirely? She looked into his eyes, dark eyes meeting her own levelly and candidly. 'Yes,' she said slowly, 'I believe you have,' and the words seemed drawn out from her without her willing it.

He drew in a breath and let it out again. 'Whew! That's a relief. It means that the first hurdle is crossed. Now, will you answer my question. Is there anyone special in your life? I think you know what I mean.'

She looked away from him. Was she crazy if she answered the question, not knowing what all this was leading to? She only knew that when she looked into his face, so serious now, she couldn't believe anything really bad of him.

She shook her head. 'No. I've got used to relying on myself. I was brought up in a children's home, I told you that. My father died when I was a baby. My mother——' she stopped, swallowed, and went on firmly '——my mother took me to the children's home one day when I was about Jules's age. She told me she would come back for me very soon.' She clenched her hands hard. 'She never came back. After a time I had to accept that she wasn't going to come back.'

'You never found out why? You never asked?'

'I—I couldn't talk about it.' The memory of that agony, all those years ago, was still with her. The bitter loss—the rejection—she had accepted it, as the years passed, but the wound had never really healed. She had just schooled herself not to think about it. 'Please——' she said now, painfully, biting her lip hard, as tears welled into her eyes.

He put out a hand and covered hers warmly. 'I'm sorry, Polly, I didn't mean to upset you.'

'You haven't. It's just that—that I've never——' She had never spoken to anyone before like this. To have done it now—to have given her deepest feelings away to a stranger—it was unbelievable.

She drew away slightly. 'I'm not looking for sympathy,' she said. 'I've managed very well on my own so far.'

He smiled faintly. 'Yes, I believe that. You're an independent little cuss, that's one of the things I like about you, Polly. Thank you for telling me all this. It makes what I have to suggest to you a little easier.'

Suddenly Polly had the strongest feeling of alarm. Whatever the job this man was going to offer her she ought not to accept it. Every hour she was in his company increased the helpless feeling of being drawn into something that was going to end in loss and black unhappiness.

She swallowed. 'I think I should say, straight away, Mr St Just, that I really want a teaching job in a school. You're going to ask me to go on looking after Jules, aren't you, and I don't——'

He leaned towards her and placed a hand over her lips. 'You do rush on so, don't you? Why don't you wait and hear what I have to say? Yes, I am asking you to go on caring for Jules and keeping him happy and occupied until I can ease him gently into the school "situation", as I believe the jargon has it. But that isn't the whole of what I'm asking.' He paused and looked straight at her, and she couldn't begin to read his expression. Then he picked up her left hand and grasped the sapphire and diamond ring between his finger and thumb, twisting it backwards and forwards thoughtfully. 'I'm suggesting that you let me put a plain gold band beside this, Polly. I'm asking you to be my wife.'

The breath left her body. She sagged back against the velvet back of the sofa, deflated, staring at him out of wide blue eyes.

'I can see I've surprised you,' he went on calmly. 'The idea occurred to me this morning. After I'd seen my acquaintance at the Embassy I phoned my solicitor in London and had a long chat with him about the possibility of my getting legal custody of Jules. Of course, I couldn't explain everything, but in effect he told me that it might depend to a great extent on what sort of a home I could offer the boy. I gather,' he went on dryly, 'that a bachelor establishment would not be looked upon with particular favour with the powers that be. Even a housekeeper or a governess wouldn't necessarily fill the bill. What they would be looking for would be a real home with a real family. So what do you think? Would you help me to provide that for him?'

Polly found her voice. 'No—no, I couldn't. It's impossible.'

'Why is it impossible?' he enquired reasonably.

'We couldn't get married. We don't love each other.' Oh, but I could love you all too easily, a voice inside her wailed, and what would that bring but misery?

'Love!' he said grimly. 'Love isn't all it's cracked up to be. I shan't fall in love again. Once was enough—I've been inoculated for life. But there's more to marriage than romantic love. Think how much this would bring to both us.' He leaned towards her, warming to his subject. 'For me it would mean that I could almost certainly get custody of Jules, as his mother appears to have deserted him. It would mean that I could leave him happily in your care and get on with my work, which I've neglected shamefully just recently. For you—well, at worst it would be a job—temporary, if that's how you wanted it. You'd be giving the boy security and I think that would give you pleasure and satisfaction. I've seen how he relies on you and turns to you all the time. And, not to put too fine a point on it, you'd be giving yourself security too, while you look around and find out what you really want to do with your life.'

Polly shook her head. 'I can't take it in all at once,' she said. And then, partly to gain time, she added, 'What about Madame Brunet?'

'You don't need to worry that kind little head of yours about Madame Brunet,' Piran told her. 'I have an agent in Paris—Paul Dufrais—who looks after my affairs here—has done ever since Maurice died. It was he who informed me of my sister-in-law's remarriage. Paul will keep in touch with Madame and see that she has somewhere to go and someone to look after her if necessary, when she comes out of hospital. Her precious daughter has been told of the position, but I'd be surprised if she comes hurrying back from the U.S. She'll leave everything to me, as she has done before. So—what do you think of my plan, Polly? Will you give it some thought? You don't have to decide straight away, you know. Let me know when we get back to London tomorrow.'

'I—I don't see how I can agree,' Polly began. 'Marriage shouldn't be a—a business contract, with each of us calculating how much we would gain out of it.'

He smiled at her ruefully. 'You're sweet, Polly. And kind. And pretty. And you have a perfect body—I know because I've seen it. I wish I could tell you that I'd fallen in love with you, but I can't. At least I've been honest.'

'Yes,' Polly sighed. She wished she could be equally honest with him, but that was out of the question.

Piran stood up and took both her hands, pulling her to her feet. 'Sleep on it,' he said quietly. 'And remember, we have a good deal to offer each other, even if it isn't undying love and happiness-ever-after. Goodnight, *chérie*.' He leaned forward and kissed her on her forehead. 'There!' he smiled, drawing away. 'That restraint is a proof of my good faith. Sleep well, Polly.'

He went out and closed the door.

Sleep well! Polly scarcely slept at all. She tried to persuade herself that she was turning over Piran's extraordinary proposal—weighing up the pros and cons for herself, while also taking into account young Jules's welfare which, she was forced to admit, had quickly become a very important matter to her. There is nothing so strong as fellow-feeling to arouse the deepest sympathy. 'I know how you feel,' when it is said truthfully, provides the link between human beings that makes them human. Polly didn't put it in so many words, but she was dimly aware that by helping Jules she would also be helping to heal her own wound of so long ago.

But marriage to Piran St Just? To this fabulously attractive man who would merely be using her for his own ends, as he had frankly, almost brutally, admitted? There was no way she could think reasonably about that. She only knew that when she was in his company everything was fresh and shining, like a new-minted coin. When he went away it was as if a shadow had fallen across her eyes, and when she saw him again her whole body leapt in wild response. Just the sound of his voice sent tremors coursing through her. There wasn't a moment when he wasn't in her mind, and when she was near him she had this insane longing to touch him, to go into his arms. If this was love, then she was deep, deep in love with the man. And all this after only a couple of days! How would it be if she were living with him? If they were sharing days together and—face it, Polly—nights too? She kept on hearing his voice saying, '—and you have a perfect body, I know because I've seen it,' in that quizzical, cool voice. Oh no, he didn't need to keep on stressing the fact that he wasn't in love with her—that was all too painfully obvious. He would sleep with her if he felt like it. In that, too, he would use her for his own purpose. There would be no lovely sharing of tenderness, no fusion of mutual passion. Only—for him—the satisfaction of a physical need. And for her? She couldn't begin to imagine.

From somewhere there came into her mind a saying that she had heard somewhere: 'There is always one who kisses and one who proffers the cheek.'

She shivered and pulled the bedclothes closer round her, although the night was warm. She must decide— she *must* decide.

What she didn't know was that she had already decided.

Heathrow seemed even busier than when Polly had started out on her holiday, not much more than a week ago. But then she had been alone. Now she had Piran beside her, organising everything, and Jules clinging to her hand trustingly, his dark eyes wide with wonder at this new experience, but not, Polly was relieved to note, frightened any longer.

There was a long wait at Customs, but at last they were through and Piran was looking for a taxi. They were going, he had informed Polly, to his godmother's home in Hammersmith. 'Her name is Alice Ashton, she's an artist—a portrait painter—and she has a studio that's in constant danger of falling into the river.' His lips twisted with affectionate amusement, and Polly, who had got to the stage when she could sometimes interpret his expression, had the feeling that this godmother of his was someone special to him.

The taxi dropped them in an alleyway and Piran carried his bags and Polly's while she managed the small holdall she had packed with Jules's clothes and one or two books that he had pleaded to be allowed to take with him. They passed under an archway, through a covered passage and out again on to a wharf where the Thames washed against stone walls that looked as if they had stood there for hundreds of years. A small boat was tied up against the wall and on the far side of the river a line of willows stood vaguely outlined in the gathering mist. Polly shivered in the damp, cool air.

'Not far now.' Piran glanced over his shoulder to where Polly and Jules were trailing behind. 'Tired, you two?'

'We're O.K.,' Polly told him, but she glanced down at Jules's bent head and dragging feet. He had been over-excited on the plane journey and now the reaction was setting in. The strangeness of everything was beginning to have its effect on him, and she only hoped that Piran's godmother would prove sympathetic and understanding.

'These are all artists' studios.' Piran stopped outside a cluster of buildings on his right and took a key from his pocket. 'Alice loves it here, she wouldn't work anywhere else.' He paused for a moment, his eyes on Polly's pale face. 'You'll like Alice,' he said, 'she's a grand person.'

He pushed open the door, disclosing a steep flight of wooden steps, and called upwards, 'Hi! Anyone in? We're here.'

A figure appeared at the top of the stairs. From below she looked to Polly to be tall and gaunt, with a voluminous smock flowing round her and greying hair that spiked untidily from her head. A voice, deep for a woman, called gruffly and joyfully, 'Splendid! Come on up.'

Piran turned and lifted Jules in his arms, carrying him up the steep steps. He put him down in front of his godmother. 'Success! Success!' His voice was triumphant. 'I return with a nephew—and what's more, a fiancée.' He put his arm round Polly's shoulder and drew her forward. 'Alice, this is Polly. Polly—Alice.'

Alice Ashton put one paint-stained hand to her forehead and regarded her godson in comical bewilderment. 'My dear, you should have warned me!' She turned to Polly. 'Forgive me, Polly, this is something of a bombshell. But a very pleasant bombshell, I hasten to add.' She had a wide, humorous mouth which was smiling at Polly now in such an easy, friendly way that Polly found herself relaxing and grinning back as she said, 'I feel a little shattered myself just at present.'

'And this is Jules. How do you do, Jules?' Alice offered her hand to the little boy, who grasped it politely and said, 'Very well, thank you.'

Alice looked up at Piran. 'Enchanting!' she

murmured, and he nodded in a pleased way.

They all went into an enormous room, part of which
was furnished as a studio and part as a living room. A
wide window overlooked the river and the variety of
craft passing along it. Jules was immediately fascinated
and stood peering out at a canopied pleasure boat,
probably returning from Kew. Alice led the way to the
far end of the room where armchairs were arranged
round a log fire burning in an open grate. Piran leaned
an elbow on the mantlepiece, smiling down at this
godmother with a wicked smile. 'Surprised you, did
we?'

'Surprised! I need to get my breath back. You
wretch, why couldn't you have warned me?' She
turned to Polly. 'There don't seem any appropriate
words for a situation like this. I can only say Welcome,
my dear, and I'm simply delighted. Now sit down,
both of you, and I'll make tea and you can tell me
all your plans. You're not going to dash down to
Dorset straight away, are you, Piran? It would be
lovely if you could all stay here for as long as you
like. I've got a quite respectable spare room, Polly,
that you could share with Jules, and Piran would
have to shake down on the studio couch in here.
What about it?'

Answering for them both, Piran said, 'That's very
handsome of you, Alice dear, and—speaking for us
both—may I say we'll be delighted to accept your
offer. As for our plans—well, we want to get home as
soon as possible, but we think it would be rather jolly
to have the wedding here in London, where you—as
my nearest and dearest—could be present. I'm not
quite sure how long notice one has to give, but I
should think that if we got going tomorrow we should
be able to arrange the wedding for about three days
hence!' He turned to Polly and put an arm tightly

round her shoulder. 'How about it, darling? That wouldn't be hurrying you too much, would it?'

Polly stood holding on to the back of a chair as her knees suddenly seemed to disappear. She was vaguely conscious of the happily untidy room around her, with its canvases stacked against the wall, of the smell of oil-paint and the apple logs burning on the fire; vaguely conscious that both Piran and his godmother were turned towards her, waiting for her reply.

It's too quick, she thought desperately. I haven't had time to decide and now he's tricked me into this, it's not fair. It's just like his arrogant assumption that everyone will agree to do as he wants. I don't know—oh, I don't know—! Plain common sense demanded that she should wait longer before she made up her mind.

Jules came running across the room, his face beaming. 'I like it here,' he announced. 'Please can we stay here, Aunt Polly? Uncle Piran?' He looked pleadingly from one to the other of them.

Piran's dark, hooded eyes were boring down into Polly's, and there was a questioning half-smile on his lips. She was conscious of nothing but the two of them standing there, linked together in some strange fashion—but not by love.

'What do you say, Polly? Jules and I are agreed that we should accept Alice's invitation and thrust ourselves upon her until our wedding. I think that would be a delightful idea, don't you, sweetheart?'

The dark eyes were still holding hers, turning her bones to water. Her mind was incapable of thought; she only knew that whatever the risk she couldn't say the words that would mean the end of this extraordinary situation. The prospect of never seeing him again if she did was totally unbearable. She drew in a quick breath and commonsense went out of the window.

'Oh yes,' she said. And turning to Alice, 'Thank you so much. I think that would be a delightful idea.'

CHAPTER SIX

'TURN round a bit further. That's right—hold it there.' Alice, a pincushion beside her on the floor, knelt beside Polly at the living-room end of the big studio, making final adjustments to the outfit that Polly would wear for her wedding tomorrow.

Polly stood as still as she could (which wasn't very still as she was suffering from acute nervous jitters) while the soft material took its final shape around her slender body. Alice had come with her yesterday to one of London's most prestigious stores, and when Polly appeared from the fitting room wearing the suit of softest delft-blue corduroy with a shimmering frill of white crêpe-de-chine showing at the neck against the delicate fragility of her skin, Alice had clapped her hands together and declared immediately that they need look no further. 'It would have to have a few minor alterations, but I'd gladly undertake to do those this afternoon. Don't you agree it's just perfect, Polly?'

Polly had regarded her reflection in the long, gilt-framed mirror dubiously. The waisted jacket emphas-ised her youthful figure and the full skirt swung round her slim legs, making her ankles appear even more fragile. 'You don't think it makes me look a bit—sort of—young and—well—ingenuous?'

'It makes you look delicious,' Alice declared emphatically. 'My godson will want to eat you up on the spot!'

Polly, who, after two days and a half in Alice's company was beginning to get used to her colourful and sometimes abrupt mode of expression, smiled faintly. It would be nice, she thought, if she could believe that. But she had grave doubts about whether Piran would even notice what she was wearing when they faced the registrar side by side tomorrow morning. Ever since she had agreed—or been tricked into agreeing—to marry him, he had seemed to lose interest in her. There was nothing she could put her finger on, he was polite and reasonably thoughtful. But the comradeship, the sense of sharing an important enterprise, had dwindled away. He had left her with Alice most of the time—'to arrange about clothes and things', he said vaguely, while he took Jules around with him to show him the sights of London. Jules seemed quite happy to be with his uncle now and, although he was always pleased to return to Polly, he didn't cling to her as he had done at the beginning.

But Polly was grateful that Alice was interested in the wedding, even if Piran wasn't, and the blue outfit was decided upon then and there and taken back to the studio for the necessary alterations.

'I shan't need anything else,' Polly declared as they waited for a taxi to take them back to Hammersmith. She had insisted upon paying for her wedding dress herself and she didn't dare tot up how little remained in her bank account. 'Piran bought me—I mean, I bought quite a lot of things in Paris. As we're going straight to Piran's home in Dorset after the wedding I can put everything together then, and see what else I shall need for a country life.'

'Yes, of course,' Alice agreed, but she looked rather hard at Polly and if a taxi hadn't appeared just then Polly thought she might have asked one or two awkward questions.

That was yesterday, and Alice had been as good as

her word. She had worked on the alterations to the suit most of the afternoon and by this morning it was finished, except for a slight adjustment to the hem. Now she scrambled to her feet and drew back, examining her handiwork as she might have examined one of her own pictures, her eyes half closed. 'Exquisite!' she pronounced. 'It's almost the exact colour of your eyes, Polly, and that always has a magnetic effect. Take it off carefully now and I'll make some coffee for us. Piran and Jules should be in before long.' Piran had taken Jules out early this morning to show him the Houses of Parliament and the Changing of the Guard.

The phone rang as Polly was easing out of the blue skirt. Alice went across the studio to answer it. 'Yes? Oh hullo, Piran—yes—yes, Polly's here, would you like to speak to her?—Oh—O.K. then, we'll see you later on.'

She replaced the receiver slowly and thoughtfully and came back across the studio. 'Piran,' she said. 'Just to say that they won't be back until later. He's taking Jules to the Barbican for lunch and then on to a concert for young people there this afternoon.'

'That'll be nice for them,' said Polly, stepping into her pants. She had an ache inside that she couldn't quite analyse. Perhaps it was foolish, but she was beginning to feel left out—almost redundant. The three of them had had such fun in Paris. They had been almost like a family. And now—now—Piran hadn't even bothered to speak to her on the phone. She turned her head away quickly, biting her lip.

Alice gathered up the blue skirt and draped it over her arm. She stood looking at Polly's back for a moment, then she said in her gruff, rather abrupt way, 'You *are* happy about this marriage, aren't you, Polly?'

Polly pulled her sweater over her head, smothering

her reply. 'Oh yes, of course I am.'

Alice stood for a moment longer, frowning. Then she collected the coffee tray from the kitchen and set it on the table before the fire.

'Sit down, Polly.' She poured coffee into two china mugs and passed a cup to Polly, who had flopped down on the white rug, her legs curled under her. 'My dear child, it's quite clear there's something bothering you, and if it isn't merely pre-wedding nerves—which I'm pretty sure it isn't—don't you think you'd better tell me what it is? I've watched you and Piran since you arrived and I get a rather odd feeling about this marriage.' Suddenly her gruff voice became softer and she went on more slowly, 'You know, Polly, Piran's very dear to me, I was with him and his brother for a long time after their parents both died abroad. I know him pretty well—I know about his first marriage too, and what a tragedy that was! I must say it was quite a facer when he turned up and announced that he was going to marry again; frankly, I never expected him to.'

She watched Polly's face as she went on calmly, 'This isn't idle curiosity, Polly. You've told me that you haven't any family of your own, and I feel there might be some way I could help. There, I've said my say, now you can tell me to mind my own business, if you so choose.'

Polly turned a grateful face up to the older woman. She had a warm feeling that she had found a friend— perhaps the first real friend that she could remember having. 'It *is* your business. You're Piran's nearest relative—he's told me that, and I guess that he thinks the world of you. I'm sure you understand him much better than I do. Has he told you how—how it all began?'

Alice shook her head. 'Not a word, and of course I

haven't asked him. One doesn't question Piran. If he wants to tell you something then he does, otherwise——' she spread out her hands with a shrug.

'He hasn't mentioned that we met in Paris, only a little more than a week ago?'

'A *week*?' Alice's voice rose by several tones. 'You mean—you've known each other a week and you're going to get married tomorrow?'

Polly smiled ruefully. 'Crazy, isn't it?' She smiled wryly. 'Well, if Piran hasn't told you how it all happened then I think I'd better.'

Alice picked up the blue skirt and threaded a needle. 'I think, my dear child, that you had,' she said.

Every single detail, from the first moment that Madame Brunet had yanked Jules up into the coach, was engraved on Polly's memory. Even so, it wasn't easy to find all the right words, and there were bits that had to be left out, if she were to keep some semblance of self-respect. Alice sat quietly sewing and sipping her coffee while the recital continued, and when it was finished she was silent for a long time.

She oversewed the final stitch and patted the hem. 'There! That's done,' she said, and hung it over the back of the chair.

There was another silence, so long that Polly began to think that she was to have no response to her story, but then Alice lifted her head, looked hard at her, and said, 'So—this is what used to be known as a marriage of convenience? In the words of a song that was a hit in my young days—"A fine romance, with no kisses"?'

Polly felt her cheeks go pink and leaned nearer to the fire. 'You could say that.'

'And Piran has made a point of being bluntly honest—telling you that he isn't in love with you? That he needs you to be a sort of glorified nanny-governess for Jules? And so that he can produce a credible family when he applies for legal guardianship of Jules?'

Polly nodded.

'But of course you're in love with him, Polly?'

Polly gasped. 'Why should you think——'

The older woman leaned forward and patted her shoulder. 'Why else would you be marrying him, my dear?' she said matter-of-factly. 'Not for security—you're young and attractive and accustomed to standing on your own feet. Not even for Jules's sake, although I can see that you're very fond of him and he of you. So——?'

Polly pulled a wry face. 'I can see it wouldn't be any use trying to take you in, so—yes, I'm in love with him.' There was an odd relief in admitting it in so many words.

'Hm.' Alice finished her coffee and put down the mug. 'I don't suppose you realise just what you're taking on, do you, my child?'

'Does anyone, ever, when they get married?'

Alice smiled. 'Intelligent and practical as well as pretty! I hope Piran recognises the value of his bargain. But seriously, Polly, it's a big gamble for you. His first marriage was a continuing trauma—enough to put any man off for life. Bianca was—well, she was a raving beauty. Dark, exotic—Italian blood somewhere, I think. He met her in Monte Carlo and they fell passionately in love and married almost immediately. Then he brought her back to live in a quiet Dorset village and expected her to get on with amusing herself while he shut himself up to write his books. Naturally, Bianca was not amused. After a time she seemed to get almost frenetic—she'd go off for days and he'd never know where she was—London, Paris, New York even. Anywhere that would pander to her almost unbalanced need for frivolity and distraction. She brought her trendy friends to the house and they nearly drove Piran crazy. In short, the marriage was going on the rocks. Then it appeared that they were going to have a child.'

'Oh!' Polly breathed a sigh, clasping her hands round her knees, her blue eyes wide. So much about Piran was being made understandable at last.

'In due course a son was born,' Alice went on. 'Piran was ecstatic. I think he imagined that Bianca would settle down now to being a mother. But not on your life! Instead, she seemed to get wilder than ever. I suppose she felt she was finally trapped, I don't know. When the little boy was about six months old Piran came to see me to say she had asked for a divorce. He was terribly upset.'

There was a long silence. So long that at last Polly asked gently, 'And did they—get a divorce, I mean?'

Alice shook her grey head. 'They didn't have to. I heard afterwards what happened. One day the nurse that Bianca had engaged to look after the child gave notice and left on the spot. There was a scene with Piran—Bianca expected him to look after the baby while she went off to a party. The child was cutting some teeth and was fretful. Piran had a deadline for a book, and he refused to take over. In a temper, Bianca took out the car and the child with her. She crashed into a tree, and they were both killed.'

Polly sat numbly silent, not able to think of anything to say, trying to take in all that she had just heard.

'So you see, Polly,' Alice went on finally, 'that you're taking on quite a formidable job. And, my dear——' she shook her head with a wry smile '—if you're building up any romantic hope that Piran's going to discover that he's fallen in love with you, I'd advise you to forget it. I know my godson fairly well and he's grown a very hard shell over his emotions. Also—and this is as important as you care to regard it—I've got a shrewd idea that he's been taking his women where he found them, if you know what I mean. If that sounds cruel, it's because I like you, and I'm afraid you're going to be badly hurt if you expect too much. Couldn't you suggest to Piran that you wait for a while before taking the drastic step of getting married?'

Polly stared into the fire, watching a log gradually turn from glowing red to dead grey ash. At last she shook her head. 'Thank you for telling me,' she said, 'but I can't back out now.' She looked up at Alice with a twisted little smile. 'We'll get married tomorrow and I'll just have to take my chance, won't I?'

'Now to work.' Piran opened his briefcase beside him on the seat of the first-class carriage and took out a large ring-folder equipped with a thick pad of paper. His eyes fixed on the top sheet of paper, covered with black scribbles, he took a gold Biro from his pocket and unscrewed the top thoughtfully.

Then he seemed to become aware of Polly, sitting opposite him, with Jules beside her in the otherwise empty carriage—Jules looking very spruce in his new grey shorts and white shirt, with the little black bow tie.

'You O.K.?' he said absently.

Polly fixed a smile on her lips, reminding herself that this wasn't a real honeymoon that they were embarking upon. 'We're fine, aren't we, Jules?' she said cheerfully, putting an arm round the little boy, who was beginning to look very sleepy. It had been a long and exciting day for him already.

It had been a long day for Polly too, and the whole day, from the moment she got out of bed this morning

after an almost sleepless night, had had a hazy
unreality about it.

The ceremony itself, in spite of the flowers that
Piran had produced for Alice and herself and in spite
of the potted plants and the stiff vase of chrysanthemums adorning the mahogany table in the
registrar's office, had had a dry, businesslike flavour,
so that Polly couldn't take in the fact that she and this
tall, elegant individual standing beside her, this
almost-a-stranger, were actually being made man and
wife. The fact that it was merely a legal contract was
abundantly clear to her.

She drew Jules closer, so that he leaned comfortably
against her, and saw his eyes begin to droop. It would
pass the time if she could sleep too.

'How long is the journey?' she asked Piran.

'Hm?' He raised his eyes from the writing pad,
staring blankly at her. 'What did you say?' he added
irritably.

'I asked how long the journey would take,' repeated
Polly, wishing she hadn't spoken in the first place.

'About two hours, we're due at Wareham at seven
forty-something.' He looked pointedly at the pile of
glossy magazines on her lap, where he had tossed them
when they boarded the train at Waterloo. 'Can you
amuse yourself for that time?' There was an edge of
sarcasm to his voice.

'I expect so,' said Polly. 'Do I have to ask your
permission to speak to you?' He could take that as a
joke—or not, as he wished.

He didn't take it as a joke. He ran his fingers
through his dark, rough hair in an exasperated fashion.
'Oh, my God, we're not back to that again, are we?'
Before Polly could think of a reply he went on, 'Now
look, Polly, I'm a writer, you know. My time's
valuable, you must understand that. When I say I'm

going to work, I mean just that. Work—and no interruptions. Understood?' He lowered his head to his work again.

Polly glanced down at Jules. His head had sagged against her and he was fast asleep. So she didn't have to be careful what she said to Piran, did she?

She looked at him now, sitting opposite in the new dark grey suit and white shirt he had bought for the occasion of his wedding. She hadn't seen him wearing a suit before and it seemed to make him a complete stranger. An elegant, disturbingly handsome stranger. But an intimidating stranger, just as he had been the first time she set eyes on him. She looked at the heavy eyelids, the hard line of his mouth, and a sudden fear wriggled deep inside her. If she let him walk all over her, then she was lost.

She smiled sweetly. 'I take it the honeymoon is over?'

His brows went up, and she saw that her small shaft had reached its mark. He looked down for a moment at the open writing pad on his knees and then, abruptly, snapped it shut. 'What had you in mind for a honeymoon?' he enquired. 'Moonlight and roses?'

She appeared to consider that. 'Sounds delightful, but—no, I don't see you as a moonlight and roses sort of bridegroom.'

He leaned back and surveyed her under lowered lids. 'What sort of a bridegroom am I then?'

Polly pursed her lips. 'When I first saw you, standing outside the coach glaring up at Madame Brunet, I thought you looked like a brigand.'

'Ah! Now we're getting somewhere, are we? You're looking for a desert sheik for a bridegroom? You think I'm the ravaging type?'

This was fooling, of course, but she had started it, so she had to go on. She appeared to consider the question, her eyes wandering over his face; the rough black hair, the bronzed skin; the stubborn chin that already was beginning to show a faint shadow.

She grinned. 'Let's say I think you're a man who has to shave twice a day.'

A look of outrage crossed his face and for a moment her stomach contracted. Was he the type to take umbrage at a little teasing?

Then a smile pulled at his long mouth. 'Damn you, Polly St Just,' he said suavely. 'You and your pinpricks—you get under my skin.'

'In the nicest possible way, I hope?' She made a great play of fluttering her long, gold-tipped lashes up at him.

'We'll have to wait and see,' he said darkly. 'And now, if you please, may I get on with a little work? If I don't catch up on schedule everyone around will suffer—you most of all, probably.'

'You have my permission,' she said demurely, and laid her head back against the cushioned seat.

He had called her Polly St Just. It sounded odd, but it sounded exciting too. She was his wife—Mrs St Just. Somehow—she had no idea how—she had got to make the marriage work, make it a real, happy, sharing partnership. Never mind if he couldn't say, 'I'm in love with you.' Perhaps one day he would—or if he didn't she could fall back on the old cliché and persuade herself that she had enough love for two.

The train rattled along, the landscape outside the window turned from green to grey. The lights came on in the carriage. Piran's dark head was lowered over his work. Polly made an attempt to read one of the magazines, but soon she lay back and closed her eyes and the events of the day unreeled themselves before her like a colour movie. Driving to the registrar's office in a sumptuous hired car, Piran and herself on one side and Alice opposite, looking unfamiliar and most distinguished in a dress of aubergine corded silk, her grey hair persuaded into a neat coil, her long, tapering fingers for once devoid of paint stains. Jules sitting very straight beside her, silent and awed, seeming to be aware of the solemnity of the occasion. Meeting Piran's solicitor, Aubrey Pont, at the registrar's office—a youngish man with crinkly golden hair and a voice that held laughter lurking in it. Polly had liked him on sight.

After that the colour film became a little mixed-up, like a dream sequence. The waiting room, the scent of the rosebuds Polly was carrying and the yellow carnations in the men's buttonholes mingled with that of furniture polish and the gas fire hissing in the grate; the short address by the registrar, the process of signing, the handshakes and kisses. Then the restaurant meal with more flowers and far too much champagne for Polly's unsophisticated taste. The farewells at Waterloo Station—Alice and the nice solicitor, Aubrey, waving through the window of the first-class carriage.

The film came to an end, passing over into the present moment. The train rushed on through the darkness. Piran bent over his writing block, mental concentration in every line of his face, utterly oblivious to everything but his work. Beside Polly, Jules slept the sleep of a tired child. The train wheels beat their tattoo, saying, 'You're married—you're married—you're married——' In the monotony there seemed to be a faintly taunting sound.

Polly eased her arm round Jules, to make him more comfortable. This, she reminded herself, was what she was here for. He stirred in his sleep and cuddled closer. She rested her cheek for a moment on his soft hair, and presently she, too, slept.

They were met at Wareham station by a ginger-haired, cheery-looking young man, driving a sleek grey Mercedes.

'How's things, Joe?' Piran greeted him as together they stowed the luggage in the boot of the car. 'You and Mrs Joe got my message?'

'Yes, Mr St Just. Glad to see you back—the missus has got everything ready for you, and a meal too. She's up at your house now, she said she'd stay until you arrived.'

'That's very good of her.' Piran turned to Polly, who was blinking around her in the quiet little station yard. She hadn't got her bearings yet, having only just been wakened as they came into the station. Never did she remember having slept so long or so soundly on a railway journey. Jules had slept all the time, too, and Piran had carried him out and deposited him, still only half awake, in the back seat of the big car. 'Polly, this is Joe Upshall, who helps me out in all sorts of ways in his spare time. Joe, meet my wife.'

'Hullo, Joe.' Polly held out a hand, and he took it rather shyly. 'Very pleased to meet you, Mrs St Just.'

Piran held open the back door of the car for her to get in beside Jules. 'I'll drive, Joe,' he said, 'I can't wait to get my hands on the wheel again after making do with a hired Fiat for the last month.' He slid into the driving seat and ran his hands over the wheel as if he loved it. Perhaps, thought Polly sadly, he was a man who loved his car more than his wife. Certainly, as they drove through the darkness, with the powerful headlights showing up what looked like open heath-land, he talked cars to Joe, sitting beside him, all the way.

After a time they turned off the main road into a lane that switchbacked up hills and down. Polly held her breath as Piran took the tight bends at speed, but she supposed he knew every inch of this countryside, and she had to believe that he knew what he was doing. All the same, she was relieved when they finally passed through a tiny village, with lights glimmering behind drawn curtains in a row of cottages, and, after another short climb up a hill, turned into a winding drive and pulled up before an open front door where light streamed out from the house inside.

Piran jumped out of the car as a plump young woman in a pink overall came out to meet them. 'Here we are, Mrs Joe. And this is my new wife, with one very sleepy young man.' As Polly was being greeted by the plump young woman he lifted Jules out of the back of the car and set him on his feet, where he stood blinking round dazedly. 'When can I see the dinosaurs?' he asked in a surprisingly clear voice, and Mrs Joe laughed and said, 'Bless the boy, you'll be wanting your supper first, won't you? Now, you come along with me and we'll find you something good to eat.' She held out a friendly hand.

Jules turned to Polly uncertainly, but she nodded and smiled and he put his hand into Mrs Joe's and followed her into the house. Joe took two bags out of the boot of the car, and Piran lifted the other one and turned towards the doorway with a buoyant step—a man delighted to be coming home.

He's forgotten all about me, Polly thought, and it was like a physical pain just underneath her ribs. She stood beside the car, her legs refusing to move, clutching her handbag and the book that Jules had brought with him for the train journey. It was her wedding day, and her husband had brought her back to his home, but never, even in the worst days of her childhood, had she felt more alone.

Then, suddenly, as she stood watching him, Piran

dropped the bag he was carrying, turned round and came back to her. 'I'm neglecting my bridegroom's first duty, aren't I?' Before she realised what he meant to do he had scooped her up in his arms and was carrying her up the steps and through the massive front door into a large, square hall, where a log fire was burning welcomingly.

He put her down on her feet, with a grin. 'There, didn't I do that prettily? You can't fault me on that one, my darling wife.'

He was teasing her, and all she could do was smile weakly because the sudden feeling of his arms round her and the pressure of his hard body against hers had deprived her of breath. She walked over to the fire. 'This is cosy,' she said, and shivered—but not because she was cold.

Piran glanced at her pale face and said, 'You look washed out. Come along upstairs and have a rest until Mrs Joe has food ready for us.' Not waiting for a reply, he lifted their bags and led the way up a wide oak staircase. Polly followed meekly, all her rebellion fading away before the man's dynamism. Coming home seemed to have made him more vital than ever. Polly glanced round the impressive hall, with its oak furniture and huge inglenook fireplace and Mexican wall-hangings. If you had a place like this for your home, it wasn't surprising, she thought, and then— with a small shock of amazement—she realised that this was her home too.

A narrow gallery ran round three sides of the hall. 'This is the guest-room,' said Piran, leading the way into a large, square room, furnished in what Polly thought was almost extravagant luxury. White pile carpet, a canopied double bed with floor-length Sanderson window curtains to match the bed hangings. A deep lounge chair, a walnut writing desk by the window. She took it all in at a glance as Piran was saying, 'I asked Mrs Joe to get this room ready just for the moment. We can make other arrangements later on, if you like, when you've seen the whole house.'

Polly glanced at the wide silk-covered bed, and then caught Piran watching her and flushed abysmally.

He grinned. 'Don't worry, I'm not going to do the brigand chief act. My own room is next door and I shall be working pretty hard for some weeks to come to meet my deadline. I shan't be exercising my—er—conjugal rights.'

Polly was bereft of speech. He couldn't have put it plainer, could he? She really didn't interest him particularly. Perhaps, later on, when he had nothing better to do, he might consider sleeping with her. For the moment his work was far more important. She felt utterly deflated and rather sick.

She looked at the enormous bed. 'Isn't there a smaller room I could have?'

He clicked his tongue in sudden irritation. 'As I told you, Polly, this room has been prepared. For goodness' sake, don't go on about it. Now have a rest and come down when you're ready.'

He turned and went out of the room, closing the door behind him with a decisive click. Polly sank down into a deep chair upholstered in peach satin, which looked too exquisite to be actually used. She didn't quite know what she had expected, but it certainly hadn't been this—that she would be put in this enormous guest-room which looked as if it could house royalty without much further adornment. She wondered where Jules was and if he was getting anxious once again.

She was too keyed-up to lie and rest. She prowled round the room, opening doors. Behind one she found a walk-in clothes closet; behind another a luxurious bathroom, with eau-de-nil fittings and every pot and bottle of toiletries she could imagine. Another door opened into a small room that looked like a dressing-room. There was a single bed, made up, and Jules's case had been placed on a chair beside it. He would be near her at night, and that was a relief.

Polly went into the bathroom and washed her face and hands. Then, back in the bedroom, she unpacked her case, took out her own modest toilet things, and set them on the glass-topped dressing table. She brushed her hair, dabbed blusher on her pale cheeks and went out of the room on to the gallery. She would go and find Jules and reassure herself that he was all right. She stood for a moment, leaning on the carved oak baluster, looking down into the empty hall.

'Where are you off to? I thought you were going to rest.' Piran's deep voice, still irritable, came from somewhere behind her. She spun round to see him, through the open door, standing in the room next to her own, bending over a desk.

His voice, coming to her suddenly like that, always had the effect of flipping her stomach over, but she took a quick breath and replied, leaning her back against the baluster, '*You* said I was going to rest. I didn't.'

He glared at her angrily for a moment. Then he turned back to his desk, with a muttered word that she couldn't catch—which, she thought, was perhaps just as well. She hastened down the staircase, clutching the polished rail as she went, feeling that all the fiends were pursuing her. But when she reached the hall, she was quite alone. After some trial and error she found her way into the kitchen, where Jules was sitting happily in front of a big white Aga. On his knee was what looked like a bowl of bread and milk, and at his feet, gazing up at him, was a large black Labrador dog.

Mrs Joe was at the cooker, stirring something in an orange-coloured casserole dish, from which rose an appetising savoury smell. She looked slightly flustered. 'Oh, Mrs St Just, it's you. I'm afraid supper isn't quite ready. I didn't know what time you'd like it.' She was a pretty young woman, brown-haired and brown-eyed, with a fresh complexion and a cheerful look about her. Polly liked her at sight; she was the first reassuring thing she had seen in this overpowering house.

'No hurry,' she said, smiling. 'Just so long as the most important person is fed!' She went across to Jules and ruffled his dark hair. 'You look as if you've settled in, young man.'

He beamed happily at her, wide awake now. 'I like it here,' he announced. 'This is Judy.' He put a rather tentative hand on the Labrador's head and she placed one floppy paw quite gently on his knee.

'Judy's very friendly,' Mrs Joe said from across the room. 'She'll be glad to have someone to play with and take her walks. I've had her at our house while Mr St Just's been away, but she's fretted a bit.'

She gave the casserole a final stir and came across to the table for a colander of shelled peas. Then she paused, looking at Polly rather shyly. 'Joe and I wanted to say as we were so glad to hear that Mr St Just had got married, and we hope you'll be very happy, Mrs St Just. It'll be lovely to have a proper mistress in the house.' Her eyes widened and she clapped a hand over her mouth like a schoolgirl, her cheeks turning crimson. 'Oh goodness, I'm always putting my foot in it, like Joe says!' She grabbed the colander and whisked it back to the cooker.

Polly stroked the Labrador's head thoughtfully. Mrs Joe must have been here at the time of Piran's marriage to his first wife. She must have known about the tragedy, and in the circumstances her remark seemed rather odd. Oh well, it was all over now, and Polly hoped fervently that she was going to be considered a 'proper' mistress. She would do her darnedest, she vowed.

After Jules had finished his supper Polly stayed with him and together they played with the big dog. Also, she found out from Mrs Joe where things were kept in the kitchen. 'I come in each day for about a couple of hours, usually,' she told Polly. 'But if you were wanting me for longer, just at first, I could probably manage it. I live down the hill in the village—we keep the general store there, and Joe and I take it in turn to look after the counter when the other one of us is out at work. Joe does the garden for Mr St Just, you see, and sometimes drives the car, like tonight.'

Piran didn't put in an appearance and presently, as Jules began to look sleepy again, Polly took him up to his room and ran his bath and saw him into bed. It was quite like old times, at the home, when she had often helped with the younger children.

She read to him for a little while from one of his books, by which time his eyelids were heavy again. Then, after showing him the communicating door to her own room, she tucked him in and promised to leave the door to the gallery ajar so that he wouldn't be quite in the dark.

She went back into the big bedroom next door and changed the blue corduroy travelling suit for a soft woollen dress in a deep burgundy colour, one of the dresses Piran had bought for her in Paris. The mirror told her that—except for the shadows beneath her eyes—she looked confident and composed, almost like the wife of a rich and successful author. But as she left her room the butterflies in her stomach were telling quite a different story.

Piran was standing in the hall. He looked up as she walked slowly down the wide staircase and she could see from his face that he was in a better humour. Evidently the work had gone well.

He grinned. 'Very pretty!' She didn't know whether he was referring to her, or to the dress he himself had chosen. He linked his arm lightly with hers. 'Mrs Joe has prepared us something that smells very delicious. Come along and try it.'

He led her into a large dining-room with a long refectory table and ladderback chairs. Polly stared admiringly. 'What a beautiful room! I love old furniture.' She wandered round, touching the carved oak bureau, the side table with twisty legs and a marquetry top, the cabinet housing a beautiful array of Spode china. 'I sometimes used to go to Christie's sales, just to look at the lovely things there.'

Piran was watching her, an odd expression on his face. 'My parents furnished the house,' he said. 'They were great collectors. I took it over as they left it.' His face clouded. 'But not everyone appreciates old things.' He shook his shoulders as if he were shaking off some unhappy memory, and then led Polly to the long table, a hand at her elbow. 'Mrs Joe has set us close together at one end,' he grinned. 'No doubt she believes we can't bear to be apart.'

Polly shrugged. 'She'll soon learn differently,' she said in a light voice.

That exchange set the tone for the meal, which was indeed delicious—a fragrantly succulent casserole of the tenderest beef, with tiny onions and button mushrooms and a subtle flavouring of herbs. Yes, Piran agreed, Mrs Joe was an excellent cook, but mostly he did his own cooking.

'Well, you won't have to bother with that any more,'

Polly told him. 'At least I can cook for you.'

He gave her a look that she had no means of interpreting, as he poured ruby red wine into their crystal glasses. 'At least,' he echoed drily.

Mrs Joe had gone home, but had left coffee already made, and Piran carried the tray into a small room next to the dining room, where a fire had been lit. 'This is what's known as the snug,' he told Polly, 'for obvious reasons. Tomorrow I'll introduce you to the drawing-room and the rest of the house, and I'll also turn the heating on. Meanwhile, use the electric fires as you need. Most of the rooms have them.'

He explained the layout of the house while they drank their coffee, sitting on either side of the fire in leather easy chairs. He also explained the parking and shopping facilities in the small seaside town a few miles away. He might, Polly thought, have been briefing a new housekeeper—and in a way, she supposed, that was exactly what he was doing.

Finally he leaned over and put his cup on the tray. 'We won't bother with the washing-up tonight,' he said. 'Mrs Joe has promised to come in early in the morning and she'll see to it. You can arrange the domestic matters between you.' He got to his feet. 'Shall we go up now?' he suggested casually.

Polly's mouth went dry and her stomach flipped over. Had he changed his mind? Did he intend that they should spend the night together after all? Her knees felt like indiarubber as they walked up the stairs together.

She went into the large guest-room and walked across to the dressing table. Every nerve of her body registered the fact that he had followed her in and through the mirror she could see that he had flopped down on the bed and was bouncing on it like a small boy. 'Very comfy,' he remarked. 'You'll be O.K. here?'

She swallowed. 'I'm sure I shall, thanks.' Why didn't he just go away, for goodness' sake? The sight of him there on the bed, even his reflection, was turning her bones to water.

She needed to do something with her hands, so she picked up a comb and ran it through her hair. She was aware of a movement behind her and then his face appeared in the mirror beside her own. He took a strand of hair between his finger and thumb. 'Pretty hair,' he murmured.

Polly stood there as if transfixed, her heart pounding. And then she felt him lift her hair away and press his lips to the nape of her neck and a shudder ran through her body. She twisted away from him. 'Don't do that,' she said jerkily.

'Sorry.' He was laughing at her. 'It was just to say goodnight. I'll go now. Sleep well, little Polly.'

She stood where he had left her for several minutes and presently she heard the tapping of his typewriter in the next room. Like a zombie, Polly undressed, slid quickly into one of the gauzy white nightdresses that Alice had insisted on buying for her, and climbed into the wide bed. There were books on the bedside table and a lamp on a beautiful ormolu stand, but Polly couldn't have focussed on a word of print. She clicked off the light, pulled the bedclothes tightly up to her chin, and lay there shivering.

It wasn't really cold, she assured herself, it was only that she was tense and nervous. Soon she would warm up and then sleep would come, and tomorrow would be better. She would establish some sort of routine, and there would be Jules to look after. It wouldn't be so bad.

She could still hear the tapping of Piran's typewriter in the next room. He had almost certainly forgotten she was here, by this time. She closed her eyes and presently she drifted into an uneasy sleep.

CHAPTER SEVEN

IT was the old nightmare that Polly hadn't had for years, and she wasn't awake yet. She was clawing her way up endless, crumbling steps, whimpering, trying to get a hand-hold on to damp stones, slippery with mosses and rough with gravel, that cut into her bleeding fingers. From somewhere above her a great deluge of poisoned water was sluicing down on her, nearer every moment. And somewhere in the water a slimy obscene monster lay in wait for her. She felt the wetness trickling on to her face and opened her mouth to scream, but no sound came. Scream after scream died helplessly in her parched throat. Terror clawed at her as she began to waken. In the thick darkness she pulled herself up in the bed and fumbled for a light with nerveless fingers. Every second her panic increased as the blackness concealed terrible unknown threats. Light—light—she must have light or she would die a horrible death—her hands flailed around helplessly. Then there was a crash as the ormolu lamp tipped over on the bedside table and fell to the floor.

A light snapped on, flooding the room, and Piran's voice demanded, 'What in the name of all that's holy is going on in here?'

Polly stared at him, shocked and speechless, her eyes dilated in her pallid face. He came across the room and picked up the lamp, flicking the switch on and off with no result.

'Is it—is it broken?' Polly whispered.

He put the lamp down indifferently. 'The bulb's gone, that's all. What were you trying to do? Smash

the place up?' His tone was sarcastic, his whole
bearing irritable and impatient. He was wearing a silk
gown in some dark colour, the girdle tied carelessly as
if he had thrown it on in a hurry. It was obvious that
he had nothing on underneath it.

Polly turned her head away, swallowing. 'Jules—did
I wake him? Please go and see if he's all right.' She
nodded towards the communicating door.

Piran walked across and disappeared into the boy's
room. He was away so long that Polly's nerves began
to quiver unbearably. She slid out of bed and padded
on unsteady legs to the open doorway. Piran was
standing beside Jules's bed, looking down at the boy.
His back was towards her, but she could imagine the
tenderness in his face. She stumbled away as he came
back into the room, closing the door carefully behind
him. 'He's O.K. Sleeping like a dormouse.' His voice
was quite different as he spoke of Jules, quiet and
gentle.

'Oh, good.' She did her best to sound calm. 'I was
afraid I might have frightened him, just when he was
settling down so well.'

He stood quite still looking at her in silence, and her
heart began to beat with heavy thuds as she was
suddenly aware that she was wearing only the flimsy
see-through white nightdress with the lace shoulder-
straps. A honeymoon nightie, Alice had said rather
drily when she had given it to Polly. She had evidently
been hoping for the best, while remaining distinctly
sceptical about the success of the marriage.

'What was it—a nightmare?' Piran said at last, and
his voice sounded odd, neither impatient nor kind.
Bored, perhaps.

Polly nodded. 'I have them sometimes. I'm sorry I
disturbed you. I'm fine now.'

The bright overhead light cast dark shadows

beneath his cheekbones. His expression was unreadable, his eyes almost hidden under their heavy lids. His forearms showed bronzed and strong beneath the short sleeves of the silk gown, his shoulders wide and muscular. Polly couldn't take her eyes off him. Suddenly the urgency of her need for him overcame everything else, even her fear of rejection.

'That's all right, then,' he said. He turned towards the door, but his feet didn't move.

'No—no, it isn't all right.' She heard her own words rushing out and had no power to stop them. 'It isn't all right, it's all wrong. I'm cold and miserable in this great room all by myself. I'm—I'm lonely.'

She choked on the final word and the tears flooded into her eyes. She turned away from him and sank down on to the bed, and when he didn't move or speak desolation washed over her in a great wave, like the wave in her dream. She leaned forward, her fists pressed to her eyes like a schoolgirl.

Then she felt Piran sit beside her, heard his voice— soothing, as if he were speaking to Jules. 'Poor Polly, poor little girl, what have we done to you? Don't cry, there's a good child.'

She leaned against him, feeling the hard warmth of his body through the thin silk of his gown and the even thinner stuff of her nightdress, and all the extraordinary tension of the last few days drained out of her as she sobbed uncontrollably. He didn't move or speak, and it was like being in a safe haven after riding out a terrifying storm. At last the sobs ceased and she groped under the pillow for her handkerchief and wiped her eyes.

'I'm sorry,' she said in a muffled voice. 'I'm afraid I cry rather easily, it doesn't really mean very much.' She laughed shakily. 'It's my Pisces moon, you see, or that's what my horoscope says.'

His arm was holding her pressed against him, and now the relief from tension that she had felt a moment or two ago was replaced by a warm disturbance that moved urgently inside her. She tried to draw away but he didn't release his grip by an inch. 'Oh no,' he said softly, close to her ear, 'we can't let you be lonely, can we? Or cold. Not while I'm here to supply the remedy.'

He tossed back the crumpled covers and laid her on the bed. Then he walked over to the light switch beside the door, pulling off his silk gown as he went. Before darkness filled the room Polly had a momentary glimpse of a strong, naked man's body, and a shudder ran through her. Then he was beside her in the bed, easing her flimsy nightdress over her head with practised hands.

His mouth covered hers and the weight and warmth of him was pressed against her. A low moan escaped her and he lifted his mouth away from hers. His voice, deep and shaken, came to her through waves of sensation. 'Polly, is my guess right—you haven't had a man before?'

She shook her head from side to side on the pillow, hearing herself falter, 'No—no—I haven't—ever——'

He drew in a deep breath and let it out on a sigh. 'I'll be very gentle,' he breathed against her cheek, and he took her face between his hands before he lowered his mouth to hers again, easing her lips apart. His hands and mouth moved against her, caressing the smooth softness of her limbs until she was almost crazy with her need, her passion rising to his gentle arousing touch until their two bodies were locked together, moving in the primeval rhythm of the waves of the sea.

Passion rose in a mutual explosive force that left Polly lying drained and deliciously languorous, drugged with happiness that filled every part of her body and mind. Bliss, she thought sleepily, heaven, ecstasy. She hadn't known it could be so wonderful. She moved closer to Piran, burying her head in the hollow of his neck.

Time passed, she didn't know how long, as she lay half asleep, happier than she had ever been in her life. Then she was aware that Piran was moving beside her. Very gently he eased himself away and sat up. Polly's eyes had grown accustomed to the darkness now and she saw him as a shadowy figure against the faint light from the direction of the window, his features indistinct. He was reaching to the floor for his gown and standing up to slip his arms into the sleeves.

He leaned down towards Polly. 'Thank you, my dear,' he said, 'that was very pleasant.'

Had she heard aright? Polly's inside plummeted downwards. Pleasant—what an odd, hurtful word! To her their lovemaking had been earth-shattering. To him it had just been—pleasant.

He touched her hair. 'Not cold any more? Not lonely?'

She shook her head from side to side on the pillow, unable to speak a word.

'That's good, then, I'll leave you to sleep.' He went out of the room and closed the door.

Polly lay very still for a long time, her eyes fixed on the place where the door made a pale blur in the darkness, her eyes aching with unshed tears. Then, from the next room, came the faint tapping of a typewriter.

She had disturbed him at his work. He had made love to her because she had practically begged him to. Now he had returned to his work and he couldn't have shown her more plainly, or more humiliatingly, that what had happened between them had meant merely that he felt sorry for her.

Polly buried her face in the pillow and sobbed out her loneliness and hopelessness. While outside, although she couldn't see it, her Pisces moon looked on coldly over the sea.

She was wakened by Jules, jumping on to her bed like any other excited small boy. 'Aunt Polly, wake up, there's sea all round and waves, and there's a little boat and——' He paused for breath and hurled himself off the bed and rushed over to the window, dragging back the long curtains. 'Can we go to the sands this morning? My daddy once took me to the sea, but——' his forehead wrinkled '—I don't know where it was.'

Polly slid out of bed and joined him at the window. The house looked down from high ground over the sweep of a bay and it was an exhilarating sight in the morning sunshine, with the sea and sky an even, picture-postcard blue. To the left a high grassy ridge swept along the skyline and dropped down, ending in dark rock, into the water. Far to the right she could see a small town nestling above the beach and rising again to form the other enclosing arm of the bay.

'Can we go to the sands?' Jules was shaking her arm. 'Please!'

Polly smiled down at him, pushing back her tousled hair, trying not to think of what had happened last night. Never again, she vowed, would she put herself in such a humiliating position. It made her flesh creep, now, to remember how she had behaved, how she had almost begged Piran to take her in his arms and make love to her. And afterwards—he had just got up and left her and gone back to his work. It wouldn't have been surprising, she thought bitterly, if he had left a couple of five-pound notes on the dressing table.

She shook her shoulders as if she could shake off the memory. 'Yes,' she told Jules. 'Let's go down to the sea when we've had some breakfast.' She felt as if she would never want to eat again, but she was here to care for Jules, she reminded herself, and Jules looked as if he needed feeding up.

Mrs Joe had laid breakfast at a small table in the window of the snug. The table was set for two and there was no sign of Piran. Polly could hardly say to Mrs Joe, 'Have you seen my husband this morning?' so she had to appear to know where he was.

She left Jules eating his cornflakes and went back upstairs. The door to Piran's room was open and his writing desk with his typewriter on it, was unoccupied. She wondered if there was a connecting door to another room and went inside to look. There was one door only and that was ajar. She peeped inside—after all, she told herself, she was perfectly justified in entering her husband's room, so why need she feel so absurdly guilty?

The bathroom was smaller than the one attached to the room next door, but fitted just as luxuriously, in a pale amber suite. An array of elegant bottles stood on the tiled windowsill and a heavy scent hung on the air that didn't in the least accord with the astringent cologne that Polly already associated with Piran. She went forward and picked up one of the bottles—an oval glass one with an ornate stopper. Mystère de Rochas, she read, and underneath— Paris.

'Hullo,' drawled a woman's voice from behind her. 'Doing a Bluebeard's Wife act?' The words were accompanied by a husky laugh.

Polly spun round and nearly dropped the bottle. In the doorway stood a dazzlingly beautiful young

woman in a white sun-suit. What showed of her skin—
and it was a great deal—was satin-smooth and
tanned to an even coffee brown, and her hair was the
white-gold colour that set off the whole spectacular
effect.

She lounged gracefully against the doorway regarding Polly with an amused stare out of green-shadowed
eyes. 'You must be Piran's new little wife. He called
on me early this morning to tell me he'd managed to
get his young nephew back to England. And to tell me
about you. You're Polly, I guess.'

'Yes,' Polly replied shortly, resenting the woman's
manner, her tone, everything about her.

'I'm Esmée Clark, and you must call me Esmée. I'm
sure we'll be great friends. Piran's such a *very* dear
friend of mine,' she added with a smooth smile.

'Oh yes?' murmured Polly, feeling her way.

'—and naturally he came round early this morning
to explain to me about why he'd felt it necessary to be
married. I must say it was a bit of a shock. Piran's
always been like me—definitely allergic to remarriage.
But I understand it was because of the boy. Poor
Piran, he's got quite a guilt complex about that
brother of his dying in Paris, and he'd do anything to
get the boy under his wing. So I quite understand why
he had to get himself a wife so suddenly. I told the
poor darling I wouldn't hold it against him.'

She laughed again as she sauntered back into the
bedroom and slid open the door of the clothes closet.
'I'll just remove the incriminating evidence,' she said
lightly, 'and take myself out of your way. Piran's
waiting for me at my cottage.' She pulled some silky
garments down from the rail and held up a black satin
kimono, thickly embroidered with vivid birds and
flowers. 'Gorgeous, isn't it?' she crooned, stroking it
with long mother-of-pearl talons. 'Piran brought it

back from Hong Kong for me on his last visit there. He's such a generous darling.'

Polly had followed in silence and she stood beside the dressing table, her hands clenched behind her. It might have occurred to her, she thought bleakly, that Piran would have a woman somewhere in England. It had been very naïve of her not to realise that a man as vital as he was would certainly not lead a celibate life. But she hadn't expected to be confronted with his woman so soon.

Esmée pulled open drawers and swept a few lacy undergarments into the expansive white canvas beach-bag she had slung over one shoulder. 'There, that's the lot, I think.' She slammed the drawers shut. 'Happy days,' she sighed, and, meeting Polly's blue stare, she rolled her eyes meaningly and added, 'Or rather, happy nights!'

She turned to the door. 'So nice to have met you, Polly. It's been lovely having a chat, and I'm sure you'll get on well here, with the little boy to look after. You're a schoolteacher, aren't you, so you'll be able to be a real governess for him.'

She touched Polly's arm lightly as she passed, and Polly felt herself cringe away in dislike. 'Don't worry, Polly, you won't see very much of me. I never could stand that mealy-mouthed woman from the shop. And anyway, I have a cosy little summer cottage quite conveniently near. I'll be staying on longer there this year.'

She swept out of the room, leaving a trail of exotic French perfume hanging on the warm air.

Polly sank on to the bed, feeling as if a steamroller had passed over her. But after a few minutes she stood up and straightened her back. Piran hadn't offered her love when he asked her to marry him, so she had been foolish to expect anything from him but a home and a

job. Last night she had lost her head completely, but it
wouldn't happen again. From now on this would be a
job and nothing more, and as soon as Jules had settled
down happily with his uncle, and the legal proceedings
were over, she could suggest that she should quietly
fade out of the picture. She was sure that Piran
wouldn't stand in her way.

She saw nothing of Piran for the rest of the
morning. After a conference with Mrs Joe about meals
she and Jules found their way to the beach. It was a
perfect September day, the sun still warm, the fringe
of golden sand stretching away to the far headland, the
waves creaming in lazily. The holiday season was
almost over and there were few people about. Jules
paddled along the edge of the tide, chattering away
happily. Polly looked at his too-thin little legs as they
splashed through the water and a lump came into her
throat.

But he would soon fatten up into a normal, healthy
little boy of his age after a while in this lovely place.
What she had agreed to do was worth while, just for
Jules's sake, she persuaded herself. She couldn't
imagine why she had complicated it by falling in love
with Piran St Just, who quite obviously would never
be in love with her—as Alice had warned her. She
must make the best of what she had, and not go
chasing after rainbows.

'Having fun?'

Polly spun round, catching her breath, as a deep,
familiar voice came from behind her. She had never
imagined that Piran would follow them down to the
beach. She had thought he would either be working
or—amusing himself with Esmée Clark.

But her resolution held. Her voice was cool and
steady as she said, 'Oh, hullo. Yes, we found our way

to the children's paradise. All Jules needs now is a bucket and spade and some swimming trunks. The water is still quite warm enough for swimming.'

'Splendid idea. Hullo, young man,' as Jules saw him and came running up. Polly saw Piran's face change, saw the pleasure on it. This, she knew, was the very first time that Jules had run to his uncle of his own accord, happily, confidently.

'Hullo, Uncle Piran. Can I swim soon?' he asked eagerly.

'Why not? We'll all swim this afternoon. Come on, we'll go down into the town and buy some gear for you and Aunt Polly. There'll just be time before the shops close for lunch.' He turned to Polly. 'That suit you, darling?'

Polly's heart somersaulted. The little word had come out so easily, so naturally. But of course it meant nothing, she told herself firmly. Perhaps writers usually call women 'darling', like theatre people.

'I'd like that,' she said rather primly, and felt his eyes linger on her curiously, before he took Jules's hand and started up the beach.

In the busy little seaside town a few miles away they found a shop with the remains of the summer stock still on show. Piran would have happily bought up the whole shop. Everything that Jules's eyes lighted upon was immediately added to the collection of buckets, spades, beach balls, games.

They emerged finally with Piran carrying a large red bucket in one hand and a cricket bat in the other, while Polly carried the spade and the stumps and Jules hugged an enormous blue and yellow ball.

Piran glanced at their reflection in the shop window and roared with laughter. 'We'd look pretty silly if it started to rain, shouldn't we?'

But it didn't rain. The September sun continued to

pour down, and after lunch they all went back to the beach. Polly, who had never learned to swim, splashed about in the shallows while Piran gave Jules his first swimming lesson. And again the treacherous idea came into her head as it had done in Paris, that they were like a happy family, the three of them. Remember the Clark woman, she warned herself, and don't get any more foolish ideas.

But she felt a certain relief because she had been dreading seeing Piran again after last night, and as it turned out it had been made easy for her. Or perhaps *he* had decided to make it easy for her, by ignoring the incident and putting their relationship back where it belonged—on the basis of friendship.

She waded out of the water, flopped down, and began to dry her hair on a soft towel. Piran and Jules came running up over the sand and Jules was spluttering and laughing. 'Ooh, I can nearly swim, Aunt Polly! Did you see me?'

'Yes, you were *very* brave, Jules. Much braver than I should have been.'

Piran stood looking down at her from his great height. 'Haven't you ever learned to swim, Polly?' he asked, and when she shook her head he added softly, 'That's something else I shall have to teach you, then.'

There was no mistaking his meaning. Oh no, thought Polly, I won't let him patronise me—amuse himself with the naïve little nobody, while he gets his real satisfaction from the soignée, sophisticated Esmée Clark, who undoubtedly knows every trick in the book to please a man. She gave her hair a final rub, managing to hide her face as she did so. It would be so easy to give herself away—to let him read the yearning in her face.

She pulled herself to her feet, ignoring his remark, and, reaching into the beach bag she had bought this morning, took out a comb and began to pull it roughly through her wet hair. She was horribly aware of him, standing so close, of his brown skin, glistening with the sea water, of the rippling muscles of his arms and legs, the dark hair that ran thickly down his chest. The longing to reach out and touch him was almost unbearable.

'Aren't you being rather brutal with that comb?' he said in an amused voice. 'Here, let me.' He took it from her hand and began to draw the comb with gentle, rhythmical strokes through her wet hair. Polly stood very still, willing herself with all her strength not to move closer to him, every nerve in her body quivering with sheer sensual desire, heat spreading upward from her toes to the top of her head.

With an enormous effort she moved away and smoothed her wet hair down with her hands. 'Thanks,' she said coolly. 'It will soon dry—I'll wash the salt out of it when I get back to the house.'

His look was fixed on her quizzically. 'I'm glad we decided on that blue swimsuit,' he said. 'It's the right colour for you and it sets off your charming shape better than a bikini would have done.' His eyes moved over her. 'A woman should always leave something to the imagination. Or perhaps I should say, in this case, to the memory?' His eyes, his voice, were teasing.

He'd made it quite plain that last night's lovemaking was no more than a diversion to him. He needn't go to the trouble of underlining it, Polly thought crossly. She threw a towel round her shoulders and lifted her chin high as she marched ahead of him up the beach.

Back at the house, Piran went off to his room—to do a couple of hours' work before supper, he said. Jules was tired, but begged to be allowed to stay up for supper, which suited Polly very well as she didn't relish the prospect of being alone with Piran. *He*

might be able to behave as if nothing out of the
ordinary had happened last night, but she found it
utterly impossible not to remember, every time she
looked at his strong hard body and sensitive brown
fingers.

'All right,' Polly told Jules, 'you can stay up, so long
as you have a rest now. You didn't have any rest after
lunch, you know—we went off to buy our beach
things.'

Jules allowed himself to be settled down on his bed
with his dinosaur book. 'When shall we go to see the
dinosaur's footsteps?' he enquired hopefully.

'When Uncle Piran isn't quite so busy with his
writing,' Polly promised somewhat vaguely, and
closed the door on him.

Mrs Joe had prepared a cold supper, so there was
nothing for Polly to do at the moment. She would, she
thought, have a look round the rest of the house and
see if she could find a smaller bedroom for herself, as
far away from Piran's room as possible.

It turned out to be quite easy. There was a
charming small room two doors away, round the
corner of the gallery. It was modestly furnished with a
single bed, a combined built-in wardrobe and dressing
table, and a cubicle shower. This, Polly decided,
would suit her very well. An uncharacteristically
cynical thought flashed across her mind that it was
just the kind of room a nanny-governess would expect.

Very quietly, so that neither Piran nor Jules would
hear, she stole back to the big guest-room and
transferred her things. She took the sheets off the
double bed and folded them neatly for the laundry.
There seemed something symbolic about that, but she
didn't let herself dwell on it. When it was all done she
took a shower and washed her hair. She did her face in
a leisurely fashion and selected a pretty yellow dress

with long full sleeves gathered into the wrist, and a wide black kid belt that nipped in her slender waist. The long mirror-door of the wardrobe told her that she looked attractive. Not in Esmée Clark's league, of course, but that didn't matter as she wasn't competing. Piran could have Esmée, if that was what he wanted. The sure thing, she assured herself with a determined tilt to her small rounded chin, was that he couldn't have them both.

Jules's bedtime was eight o'clock. Polly came downstairs at a quarter to nine to find Piran in the snug sorting through records.

'Jules is all tucked up—will you go and say goodnight to him?'

'Surely,' he said immediately. And then, 'I thought we might have some music afterwards—what's your fancy?' He indicated the record cabinet. 'Have a look while I'm upstairs.'

Polly said hastily, 'I must clear away the supper things and wash up. Mrs Joe can't come in tomorrow morning.' A cosy session with Piran, listening to music, was the very last thing she could face.

He shook his head at her, smiling. 'Going all domestic on me, are you? I can't allow that. We'll do the washing up together afterwards if we must.' He went to the door and turned. 'Now, don't move from this room until I come back, and that's an order!'

Polly wished he wouldn't smile at her like that; it made her knees go weak. She sank down into a leather-covered chair beside the hi-fi and ran her eyes down the index of records, seeing nothing but the bold black handwriting that had to be Piran's. Decisive—self-confident—sure of getting what he wanted. You didn't have to be an expert to see that in his handwriting.

She was still examining it when he came back into the room. He came and stood near to her, towering over her, and she got to her feet nervously. 'Aren't you going to write tonight?'

He didn't reply, but stood staring at her, frowning. Just as she couldn't bear to hold his gaze any longer he rapped out sharply. 'Why have you moved your room?'

'Oh, that,' she said coolly. 'I told you the guest room was too large for me. I found a smaller one that will suit me very well.'

In his most dictatorial voice Piran said, 'I don't wish you to have that room. You'll oblige me by taking your things back.'

Polly shook her head. 'I've told you, I would prefer it. I don't care for the large guest room. It—it overpowers me.' And not only the room, she added to herself. The knowledge that you are there, on the other side of the wall, is infinitely more overpowering.

She could see the anger gathering in his face, in the dark, forbidding brows, the hard line of his mouth. He looked just as he had looked that first evening when she had walked into Madame Brunet's apartment with Jules and found him there. He said between his teeth, 'Will you do as I ask and move your things back?'

'No,' she said firmly, but she was shaking inside and she felt a little sick at the unexpectedness of this attack.

He turned abruptly. 'Very well, then, I will,' he said, and strode out of the room.

She wouldn't—she *couldn't* allow him to dictate to her like this. He hadn't even given her a reason—merely issued an order. Before she had time to let her fear overcome her she ran after him up the stairs. As she passed Jules's room she glanced inside, to see him fast asleep already. She closed the door gently and went on into the small room beyond. Piran had pulled a sheet from the bed and was sweeping her toilet things off the dressing table into it.

Polly saw red. 'H-how dare you?' she stammered, and grabbed his arm. The brushes and pots were scattered on the carpet as he dropped the sheet.

'Oh, I dare—I dare do a lot more than this,' he rasped, and he took her wrist in a steely grip that sent pain shooting right up her arm. 'Come along, tell me the truth. Why did you want to move out of the room next to mine?' His face was so close to hers that his features were out of focus as she stared up at him. Only the dark, dangerous glint in his eyes made her blood run cold.

'I—I told you, the room was too large for me. I was afraid of having another nightmare.' She took a quick breath and rushed on, 'I hate feeling I'm not in control of myself.'

He moved away a little, so as to be able to study her face, but didn't release his hold on her wrist. 'So that's it, is it? You didn't want to put any more ideas into my head—you invite me into your bed in no uncertain manner and then you move away from me as far as you can get. What exactly are you playing at, Polly?' His voice was as nasty as he could make it.

'N-nothing,' she said miserably. 'I just thought it would be better if we didn't clutter up this situation with anything—intimate.'

'Really?' he sneered. 'You didn't enjoy last night, was that it? You were disappointed? You'd hoped for—how did you so aptly put it?—a brigand chief for a husband? What did you expect of the marriage, for God's sake?' He was working himself up into a flaming rage now, shooting the questions at her one after the other, giving her no time to reply. 'Did you have some romantic idea that I might fall in love with you after all—did you want a husband who would ride up on a black charger and carry you off to ravish you? Was that the idea in your silly little head?' he shouted.

Polly put her free hand over her ear. 'Oh, stop—please stop, let me explain!' she wailed. She would have told him about Esmée, about her disgust at the idea of sharing him with another woman; she would have tried to make him understand, but he was long past reasoning with. He was shaking with anger now, almost out of control.

She tried to wriggle out of his grasp, but it was hopeless. Instead, she found her other arm gripped as he began to force her back towards the bed. 'You want to be ravished, do you?' he grated out. 'Is that what you want? Well, let's see if I can oblige you!'

The whole room was spinning round in Polly's outraged senses. She struggled with all her strength, but she might have been a small animal in the grip of a beast of the forest for all the good it did her. She was pressed down against the mattress and held there with one powerful hand, while Piran's other hand tore the yellow dress from her shoulders. She heard the thin material rip and felt his mouth hot against her breast as the dress opened and fell apart.

'Is *this* better, then, my darling wife? Is *this* what satisfies you?'

'No—please——' she moaned, as the rest of her clothing was stripped from her, but he took no notice. He pinned her down with one knee while he shrugged off his own clothes and then his weight was on her, heavy, merciless.

This was no gentle wooing as last night had been. This was all careless, thrusting, brutal masculine virility, going on and on until she cried out with the pain that was almost pleasure. Then suddenly she found resistance ceasing, felt inside her a hot mounting tide of passion that took her over completely, so that she was caught in a leaping moment of ecstasy before she collapsed limply and lay half-sobbing on the bed. She felt Piran's arm still resting on her, heard his breathing gradually quieten until he lay still beside her, very close in the small bed.

With a tremendous effort she slid away from him and pulled a nylon wrapper round her naked body. The glare from the overhead light showed her her reflection in the long mirror, her face flushed and blotchy, her hair in wild disarray. She crawled into the shower room and let the cool water splash over her hot skin until she felt blessedly cool again. Then she dabbed on lotion and powder, combed back her hair and opened the door into the bedroom.

Piran was sitting on the edge of the bed, pulling on his trousers. He didn't say a word as Polly came across the room and stood a little way away, looking over the top of his head as she spoke.

'I'd be glad if you'd leave my room immediately,' she said in a stiff little voice. Out of the corner of her eye she saw his head jerk back as if she had struck him, but still he didn't speak.

She drew in a short breath. Inside she was quivering, but mercifully her voice was quite steady as she said, 'And I want to make it clear that I won't tolerate this sort of treatment from any man. If you want me to stay here until after the legal hearing for custody of Jules I'm prepared to do that, because I promised, and for Jules's sake. But when that's over I should like to leave and you can make the necessary application for a divorce. I think the sooner we part the better, Piran, and no doubt you agree.'

He got up then, and stood glaring down at her, his shirt tossed across one shoulder, the thick black hair damply matted on his wide chest. 'Polly——' he began, 'I——' he broke off, shrugging in a gesture of angry frustration. Then, 'Oh, *hell*——' he muttered. And he turned and flung out of the room, leaving the door open behind him.

Polly went over and closed it and stood with her back to it, tears burning behind her eyes. That was it, then, the end of something that had never really begun. His taunt had been justified, she knew now that she *had* had a romantic dream that he might fall in love with her, that one day she would see tenderness in his face. But all she had ever seen was amused pity— or sometimes bitter, unreasonable anger. Nothing there to found a relationship on, and never would be. It was better that she should go when she had served her purpose.

Much better, she repeated to herself, but a black emptiness yawned in front of her, and all meaning had gone from her life.

CHAPTER EIGHT

JULES had finished his breakfast and gone out into the garden while Polly drank a second cup of coffee. A place was laid for Piran, but he hadn't put in an appearance yet. Polly didn't know, even, whether he was in the house or not, or where he had spent the night.

It had been like this for weeks now. They had lived in the same house as strangers. Piran had talked to Jules, explaining that for a time he was going to be very busy, but after that they would go on outings together and have fun. To Polly he had hardly spoken, except as was necessary for the running of the house. When he wasn't in his room, working behind a closed door, he took the car and disappeared—presumably to the 'cosy little cottage' belonging to Esmée Clark.

Polly told herself it was better like this, but sometimes she felt she would almost rather have faced his anger than this complete indifference. Fortunately she was kept very busy. She ran the house with Mrs Joe's help, and did some of the cooking. The rest of the time was spent with Jules, reading, answering his endless questions about everything under the sun, walking along the beach and over the heath that stretched for miles behind the house, with Judy the Labrador lolloping around them. The weather had changed and it was too cold now for bathing. Piran had told Jules that he had a boat, but was too busy to take it out just now.

'Uncle Piran has promised to teach me to sail it one day,' Jules told Polly proudly.

'Splendid, you'll enjoy that, Jules.' Polly made herself smile, but inside she was aching with the knowledge that she wouldn't be here to share in the enjoyment. Piran's application for custody of Jules had gone through all its stages and now it only remained to wait for the final legal decision. After that she would start making arrangements to leave. Just like giving notice in a job, and really that was all it had been. A temporary job. She told herself that all nannies ran the risk of heartbreak when they had to leave a child they had grown to love. This was something she had to face.

As for Piran—the prospect of never seeing him again was something she couldn't face yet. The yearning for him had grown no less with his indifference. The jealousy that tore at her when she guessed he was with Esmée Clark had grown no less acute. Sometimes she felt that she was bleeding to death inside herself.

She finished her coffee now as Piran came into the dining room. He nodded to her and picked up his post.

'Wait a minute,' he rapped out, as she got up to carry her cup and plate to the trolley. 'There's a letter here from Aubrey. He says everything seems to be tied up but there are more documents for me to sign. He's coming down for the weekend to stay with his parents at Corfe Castle. I suppose he might turn up here, so will you make arrangements to be in this afternoon, please, in case I happen to be out.'

'Certainly,' said Polly, in the composed toneless voice she always used now on the rare occasions when she spoke to Piran.

So—it was nearly over. She felt hollow and empty inside, dreading what was ahead in the next few days. But she would be glad to see Aubrey, Piran's solicitor, again. He was such a cheery soul and she had liked him from the first moment she met him at the wedding. She had seen a good deal of him since then. He was unmarried and spent many of his weekends at his parents' house in Corfe Castle, a village only a few miles away. He had come over several times for lunch or dinner, and to discuss legal matters with Piran. Now, she thought bleakly, there would be another legal matter to discuss—a divorce. She shuddered at the word.

But in the afternoon, when Aubrey's white coupé crunched over the gravel sweep and drew up in front of the house her spirits lifted. He came across the forecourt towards her, a tall, cheerful youngish man with crinkly fair hair and smiling eyes, and took her hand in both his. 'Grand to see you again, Polly. And Jules too——' as the little boy came running up from the bottom of the garden. 'This is a splendid excuse to get away from London for a day or two. How are you, Polly? And how's old Piran?'

'Working most of the time,' said Polly. 'He's got this deadline for his book. We don't see very much of him, do we, Jules?'

She was horrified to hear her voice quiver on the last sentence, but Aubrey merely grinned as he said, 'That's the worst of these writers. You should have married a legal boffin like me who keeps office hours, Polly. Home on the dot every evening, complete with bowler hat and rolled umbrella!'

Polly laughed, grateful that her lapse had passed unnoticed. Or was it Aubrey's tact that had covered up an awkward moment? She had wondered several times recently how much he knew of the circumstances of her hasty marriage to Piran. Piran must have told him something—Aubrey was an old friend of Piran's as well as his solicitor.

She led the way into the drawing room, which had a breathtaking view down the garden to the expanse of sea beyond. Polly had grown to love this room. She let her eyes rest for a moment on the spectacular view— the navy blue of the sea with little white crests of wave here and there, and the green headland, falling down dramatically into it at the far end of the bay. Just another thing she would miss among all the rest, she thought, and her eyes suddenly filled with tears.

Aubrey joined her at the window. 'Super view, isn't it? I always envy Piran this view.'

Polly blinked and turned quickly to the side table and he came up behind her. 'Are you feeling O.K., Polly? You look a bit under the weather.'

She swallowed quickly. 'Oh, I'm fine, thanks. I was going to pour you a drink. What will you have? Or would you rather have some tea?'

'Thanks very much, but no. Too early in the afternoon for a drink, and my mother gave me tea when I got to Corfe Castle earlier on.'

'Corfe Castle?' Jules piped up. 'That's where the dinosaur's footprints are. It says so in my book. Uncle Piran promised to take me to see them, but he's always too busy.'

Aubrey laughed. 'Shame! You'll have to come to my house some time, Jules. My father knows all about dinosaurs.'

Polly said, 'I'll go up to Piran's room and see if he's still working.'

A minute or two later she was back, shaking her head. 'He must have gone out without my seeing him. Jules and I have been in the garden.'

'Never mind, I'll wait if I may. I don't suppose he'll be long.'

An hour passed, and Piran hadn't returned. Aubrey was easy to talk to and after the strained silences in

Piran's company it was a relief to Polly to be able to make a remark without wondering, first, if it would give offence. Aubrey talked interestingly, mostly about Dorset, where he had been born and brought up. He seemed quite impressed when Polly showed a knowledge of the history of Corfe Castle, and Jules had to hear all over again about the murder of the young King Edward there and much later the siege of the castle by Cromwell's soldiers.

At last Aubrey got to his feet. 'My mother has some people coming to dinner tonight and I mustn't linger any longer, much though I'd like to. It's been great talking to a girl who's intelligent as well as charming. I've enjoyed myself immensely.' His nice grey eyes smiled appreciatively.

They moved to the front door. 'Tell Piran I'm sorry to have missed him. I'll ring him in the morning and we'll fix up to meet. He'll be glad to know that everything seems to be sewn up and it only has to be finalised now.' He glanced over his shoulder to where Jules was playing with Judy, the Labrador, in the garden. 'The letter from the boy's mother, more or less agreeing to anything, carried a lot of weight with the Court. Poor kid, she's not interested in her son, it would seem. And of course it was darned lucky for Jules that Piran met you and that he could offer to provide a real family background for the boy. That probably tipped the scale.'

Polly said brightly, 'Yes, it was very well timed, wasn't it?' She held out her hand. 'Goodbye, Aubrey, I'll tell Piran you were here and you'll ring him tomorrow.'

She watched the car disappear down the drive and went thoughtfully back into the house.

Half an hour later Piran returned. Polly was in the dining room, setting the table for supper, and he went straight over and poured himself a drink. He tossed it off and poured a second one, placed it on the corner of the high oak mantleshelf and regarded Polly in silence. He often did this now—stood silently watching her while she went about her tasks, and it made her want to scream. Now she said, without looking at him, 'Aubrey came when you were out, earlier on.'

'Ah,' he said. 'You were able to entertain him most pleasurably, I'm sure.' The words were almost a sneer.

She spun round, a bunch of cutlery in her hand. 'What's that supposed to mean?'

He picked up his glass and looked into it thoughtfully. 'I've noticed that you and Aubrey get on very well, that's all.'

'I like Aubrey,' said Polly. 'He's a very agreeable companion.'

'And I'm not, I take it?'

She began to place knives carefully on the white tablecloth. 'I wouldn't call you agreeable,' she said. 'But no doubt you don't consider it necessary to make yourself agreeable to me.' She turned round and faced him, taking her courage in both hands. He had made this opportunity for her—now she must grasp it.

'And while we seem to be on the subject,' she said calmly, 'and while Aubrey is here, I think we should consider how best to—to arrange for our marriage to end. I seem to have fulfilled my purpose, now that the custody of Jules is granted to you. He's a happy little boy now and he doesn't depend on me as he did at first. He'll be starting school after half-term, as you know, and he's already made friends with one or two of the small boys in the village.' She felt the treacherous tears prick behind her eyes and turned her head away as she added, 'I daresay he'll miss me a bit at first, but children soon forget.'

She didn't see the expression on his face, but his

voice was harsh as he said, 'And what if I don't intend that you should leave?'

The remainder of the silver fell to the table with a clatter. 'But—but it was all arranged! We said that the marriage was only going to last until you could get custody of Jules.'

'*You* said so,' Piran said curtly. 'I didn't.'

Polly felt her knees go weak and she pulled out a chair from under the dining table. This was something she had never for a moment expected. She had thought he would be glad to be rid of her, relieved to break out of the strained difficult atmosphere that prevailed when they were forced into each others' company.

'I don't understand,' she whispered, gripping the chair-back with both hands. 'Why won't you let me go?'

He shrugged and took a swig of his drink. 'Let's just say it doesn't suit me at the moment.' His voice was arrogant—contemptuous, she thought.

Suddenly Polly was blazingly angry. She rounded on him, thumping the table. 'You've got to let me go—you promised! What sort of a life is this for me here?—I don't want to stay with you. When I marry I want a real marriage, with—with love and warmth and consideration. I want a man who can love me—not a cold, arrogant—*beast*!' Her voice was shaking wildly and the tears were scalding her eyes.

'Someone like Aubrey Pont, for instance?' he sneered. Polly wondered if she had heard aright. He couldn't be—jealous, could he? No, of course not, he was just being petty. He didn't want her himself, but he didn't want any other man to look at her.

She raised her head defiantly. 'Yes, someone like Aubrey. Aubrey's a darling.'

'Aubrey's a darling!' he mimicked nastily. 'Well, at

least he's had the good sense to steer clear of marriage so far. But to get back to your request, the answer's no.'

'But—but *why*?' She had to know—somehow she must make him tell her. She beat her hands on the back of a chair. '*Why*, Piran?'

He leaned towards her and gripped both her shoulders. 'Shall I tell you why?' His eyes were sombre as they gazed into her own and she felt all the old magnetism return at his touch. She wanted, insanely, to cry out, 'No, I don't want to know anything—I just want to be near you, to see you every day, to be part of your life, on whatever terms.'

'Polly——' he began.

A movement at the french window behind them made them both spin round and Piran dropped his hands. Esmée Clark stood there, looking incredibly beautiful in a black-and-white striped silk shirt and tight black trousers, her hair gleaming silver in the evening light.

'Sorry if I'm interrupting something,' she said smoothly. She walked across the room to Piran. 'You left your watch on the shelf in my shower-room, darling.' She held it out. 'I thought you might be wanting it. Hullo, Polly, and how's the little governess getting along?'

Her smile was silky, sliding across her perfect mouth insincerely. It was a question intended to be insulting, and Polly caught her breath, stiffening at what was patently an attack. She glanced at Piran, letting herself hope for just one moment that he would defend her. She was his wife—she had the right to expect that much. He could destroy Esmée Clark with one word—one look—if he cared.

But he merely took the watch from Esmée's hand and slipped it into his pocket, saying nothing. Polly lifted her head high and went out of the room, closing the door behind her.

Up in her bedroom she sat on the bed, shivering. She couldn't take much more, she had to get away soon. For a moment, just now, she had let herself imagine that Piran might be going to suggest that they should give their marriage another chance, but of course she had been mistaken. She couldn't guess what he had been going to tell her, but certainly it wasn't that. Probably he was going to make use of her, and their marriage, in some other way that suited him. Could she turn to Aubrey, tell him the truth and ask him to help her? Was there any way she could divorce Piran, unless he agreed to it? Could she use his relationship with Esmée Clark? Everything inside her revolted against trying such a course.

She sat there until it was quite dark. Jules had gone out to tea with one of the little boys in the village—the son of the local doctor—and Piran was supposed to be calling for him. She wondered if he would remember or if he had gone off again with Esmée. But even as she wondered that she heard his car crunch on the gravel below and Jules's voice raised excitedly in the hall, telling of all he had done that afternoon.

Her whole body aching with tiredness, Polly pulled herself to her feet. There was her job to be done while she remained here. She went down to give Jules his supper and see him into bed.

She passed Piran on his way upstairs. As they met he seemed to hesitate and was about to say something, but she went straight on, not looking at him. A moment later she heard the door of his room close with a vicious slam.

Polly and Jules had supper together and Piran didn't put in an appearance at all. Afterwards she cleared away the dirty dishes, left the salad and cold meat covered on the table and devoted herself to Jules until it was his bedtime. After that she went to her room and stayed there. From this room she couldn't hear Piran's typewriter or his voice speaking into the dictation machine, and she didn't know whether he was in or out. Probably he had gone back to Esmée. She felt cold as a stone inside and her head was hot and aching. She wondered if she were going to be really ill. It seemed unlikely; she was hardly ever ill, and she certainly couldn't afford to be ill now. Tomorrow, come what might, she was going to resolve this agonising situation.

But again fate seemed to be against her. On going down to prepare breakfast she found a note propped up against the telephone in Piran's black, bold handwriting. 'Gone to London to see publisher,' it said. 'Back tomorrow, probably about midday. Piran.'

A frustrated sigh escaped Polly. She had lain awake most of the night, working herself up to a final confrontation, and now—this. She thumped the table in her exasperation. Then she thought of Aubrey. Had he gone back to London, or was he still at his home in Corfe? She picked up the telephone and as she dialled his number she thought childishly, If he's there I shall tell him everything and ask him to advise and help me. If he's gone—I don't know what I shall do. Helpless tears pricked at her eyes.

'Hullo—who's that?' a sleepy voice answered the phone. And then, on her reply, 'Polly! But how splendid!' in a much more wide-awake tone. 'You caught me sleeping in. My parents are away for a couple of days and I'm indulging myself.'

Not giving herself time to think, Polly said, 'Aubrey, are you free this morning? Could you come over—there's something——' she broke off, biting her lip hard.

There was a tiny pause. Then, 'Polly, what's up? Are you O.K.?'

She pulled herself together as Jules came running up to her. 'Oh yes, everything's fine. Piran's gone to London, and I just wondered if——' she improvised wildly, '—if perhaps you could take Jules to see the dinosaur's footprints, as you suggested.'

'Done! I'll be with you in twenty minutes flat.' There was no mistaking Aubrey's enthusiasm for the idea, and Polly breathed in relief.

It was the strangest of days for Polly. Aubrey Pont was the most charming of companions, and he set himself out to give both her and Jules a good time. First he took them back to his parents' home—a beautiful house, built of grey Purbeck stone, standing in a spacious wooded garden below the grey, broken pile of Corfe Castle high up on the hill above. The weather had turned warm again—almost an Indian summer—and they made coffee and drank it sitting on the terrace while Aubrey raided his mother's freezer and found ice-cream for Jules, and a bone for Judy. It was all so peaceful and happy and Polly felt the ragged tension of the last weeks seeping away. She lay back in her hammock chair and closed her eyes, while Jules played with Judy on the lawn, and the wood-pigeons, thinking it was still summer, called from the distance. I won't ask Aubrey yet, she thought. Let me have this last, lovely day.

And, against all the odds, it was a lovely day. Aubrey took it for granted that they would all spend the day together, and he took charge of the proceedings. Later in the morning they visited the tiny cave-like museum in the village street and Jules at last saw the fossils of the dinosaur's footsteps, to his awe and delight. After exploring the village, with its tourist shops not yet all closed for the winter, they went back to the house and put together a picnic lunch, which they ate out of doors again.

'What next?' Aubrey enquired, when Jules had had his afternoon rest on the sofa indoors. 'I suggest that we might climb up and explore the castle ruins, they're quite spectacular. Or if it's too far for Jules to get to the top we could get as far as the Martyr's Gate, where King Edward was killed. Then we'll come back here for tea, park Judy, and end the day at the Mowlem in Swanage. They're showing *The Sound of Music* once again there. How about it? Would that be too late for Jules?'

'Oh no, please, let's go,' Jules pleaded eagerly, and added in his quaint, old-fashioned little voice, 'I can sleep longer tomorrow.'

And so it came about that it was after ten o'clock as they finally drove in Aubrey's white sports car, with the hood down, and the evening scents drifting on the warm air, back along the narrow country roads towards Piran's home, Jules snuggling comfortably between them and Judy packed into the luggage boot behind. 'The hills are alive with the sound of music,' Polly sang, and Aubrey joined in, and it wasn't until the car finally turned in at the drive that she realised that the whole of this pleasant, friendly day had passed and she hadn't done what she intended to do—ask Aubrey's help.

Now the dark pile of the house rose up against the lighter velvet of the starlit sky and she knew she couldn't spoil this lovely day.

'Thank you so much, Aubrey. We've all enjoyed ourselves so much.'

The car stopped and he switched off the engine. 'Me too,' he said. 'Thank you for making the last day of my holiday so rewarding. It was a brilliant idea.' He glanced up at the house. 'Are you all alone here tonight—Piran's not coming home?'

'Not until tomorrow,' she said.

One hand on the door he hesitated, glancing down at Jules's head, drooping sleepily back against the cushioned seat. 'Polly, I have to ask you this—is everything all right—between you and Piran, I mean? I've thought lately that perhaps you weren't too happy. Tell me to shut my mouth if I'm wrong, but if there's any way I could help, then——'

Now was the moment. Now she could say, 'I do want your help, Aubrey. That's why I rang you up this morning.' And she could ask him to come into the house, while she put Jules to bed, and then she could tell him everything.

But the words wouldn't come. She heard herself laugh lightly. 'You're a dear, Aubrey, and there *has* been a bit of misunderstanding, but everything's all right now.'

Almost before the words were out a light snapped on in the hall and the front door was flung open. Piran stood there for a moment, his tall body black and forbidding against the light flooding out from behind. Then he was across the gravel in a couple of strides, and his rage seemed to vibrate in the still air.

Polly felt a grip of steel on her arm and she was yanked out of the car. A moment later Jules was beside her, clinging sleepily to her hand, not quite sure, mercifully, about what was going on.

Piran's voice was low and menacing, close to her ear. 'Get into the house and get Jules to bed. I'll deal with you later.'

Aubrey had come round from his side of the car. 'Now look here, old chap, there's no need to——'

Polly heard Piran snarl, 'Go to hell, you——' before she ran for the front door, pulling Jules along with her.

Somehow she managed to get Jules into bed, with a warm drink. She moved like an automaton, speaking to him quietly when he seemed a little nervous and upset. 'Uncle Piran was angry, wasn't he? Didn't he want us to go and see the dinosaur's footprints?'

'Yes, of course he did, darling. He was tired, that was all, he's had a long journey. You'll be able to tell him all about it in the morning. Now, you settle down and go off to sleep. It's been a lovely day, hasn't it?'

'Ooh yes,' he yawned. 'Lovely day. Uncle Piran come up to say goodnight?'

'I'll go and ask him,' said Polly.

She had to force her feet to take her down the stairs. She winced away from seeing Piran's cold, furious face, and she felt sick and shaky. But somehow she went into the snug, where she expected to find him.

'Jules is ready to settle off,' she said tonelessly. 'He would like you to go up and say goodnight to him.'

She couldn't bring herself to look at him. He said nothing at all, but turned and went out of the room. Polly put out a hand and clung to the carved edge of the mantelshelf. What should she do now? Where should she go? She couldn't stay here another night. She turned this way and that, like a terrified small animal looking for escape.

Piran came back into the room, closed the door and stood with his back to it. He looked terrible. His face was drawn and haggard, his hair tousled, and there were dark lines under his eyes. She sensed that his anger had worn itself out.

He glanced at her and away again quickly. Then he poured himself a small drink and tossed it down. Polly waited, her head throbbing.

At last he said, 'I can't take any more of this. I've been out scouring the cliffs and the heath for you for the last two hours.'

'I didn't think——' she began, but he cut in violently. 'No, you didn't think, did you? You never *would* think, you never *would* understand.' He passed a hand over his brow and rubbed a spot on his temple as if it were hurting.

And suddenly Polly realised what he had suffered when he came home and found them both gone. He must have thought that history was repeating itself, that he had lost Jules in the same way that he had lost his own son.

She longed to put her arms round him and tell him she did, indeed, understand, that she would never in this world do anything that would put Jules at risk. But her arms remained tautly by her side. He wouldn't want her sympathy. He didn't love her.

He sighed deeply. 'It isn't working out, Polly, it had better end. I'd like you to leave tomorrow. You can think of something to tell Jules.' He spoke slowly, with infinite tiredness, and it was so much worse than if he had been angry.

She said in a choky voice, 'I would like to go tonight—now.'

'Go tonight?' Piran's head jerked up. 'To Aubrey Pont?'

'No, of course not,' Polly said wearily. 'Aubrey is nothing to me except a good friend. I shall go down to the village. Mrs Joe will give me a bed for the night. I shouldn't think she'd be surprised, she must have guessed there was something wrong with our marriage. And *you* can think of something to tell Jules. I—I couldn't tell him a lie about coming back.' Jules must not suffer the agony she had suffered, waiting for her mother who promised to come back and never came. He would be sad for a time, but it would be a clean break and he would get over it, with his new friends and starting school soon and everything.

She said, 'I'll go up and pack a bag. I'll just take what I need for now. When I get settled somewhere I'll let you know and perhaps you'll send the rest on to me.' This wasn't her, talking so calmly, it couldn't be. This was a frozen shell. The real Polly was deep inside somewhere, sobbing, as her heart slowly broke.

'Where will you go? What will you do?'

She said, on impulse, 'I think I'd like to go to London. I could stay with Alice for a night or two, if that's all right with you. I'm sure she would have me.'

'Alice?' Piran looked suddenly affronted. 'She mustn't—she'd be devastated——'

Polly shook her head slowly. 'She wouldn't even be surprised. She told me all along that I was taking a terrible risk in marrying you. She wanted me to wait.'

'But you didn't want to wait?' he said, and for the first time some of the old vital Piran was there.

'I'd promised,' she said stonily. 'For Jules's sake, I couldn't go back on it.'

'Ah!' he said, and it was as if he understood something that had puzzled him. 'Very well, then, if you must go now, you must. I'll give you a lift down to the shop.'

All so ordinary! She might have been going down there to buy the week's groceries. She went upstairs and threw some things into a case. She pulled a light coat over her blue wool dress. Then she looked into Jules's room and a shaft of light fell across his sleeping face. He looked trustful, secure. Blindly, Polly closed the door gently and went downstairs.

Piran was waiting outside the front door. He put her case in the boot of the car and they drove down the hill in complete silence. When they reached the village shop he got out and carried the case up the path and put it down by the door. 'I'll wait in the car to make sure she can put you up,' he said, and turned away without another word.

Polly knocked at the door and waited. In a moment it was opened and Mrs Joe's face appeared, rosy and surprised. 'Oh, it's you, Mrs St Just. Have I forgotten something? I did bring the butter up like you asked.'

'Could I—could I come in and speak to you a moment?' Polly forced the words through her tense throat.

'Why, of course you could. Come right in.' Mrs Joe threw the door open. Then she spotted the car at the bottom of the path. 'Is Mr St Just with you? Will he——'

'No,' Polly said sharply. 'He has to go.' She raised a hand in signal towards the car, a dim shape in the darkness, with just the sidelights showing. She couldn't see Piran sitting in the driver's seat, but as she dropped her hand the powerful engine revved up and the sound of it died away, back up the hill. Very slowly she followed Mrs Joe into the cosy sitting room behind the shop. Her husband got up from his corner and switched off the TV.

Mrs Joe glanced at Polly's paper-white face and quickly away again. 'Here's Mrs St Just come to see us,' she told her husband rather awkwardly. 'Do sit you down, Mrs St Just. I've just made us some tea, it's quite fresh.'

Polly sat down and took the cup held out to her. The hot, sweet liquid loosened her tight throat a little. 'Joe—Mrs Joe——' she looked pleadingly at the couple sitting side by side on the sofa '—can I ask your help? Somehow I have to get to London as soon as I can. Tonight, if it's humanly possible.' The thought of staying here, so close to Piran and Jules, was agony. The only possible way was to put as much distance as she could between herself and them both.

She had told Piran that she would go to Alice, in London, but that she couldn't do, either. She would write to Alice, or phone, and give her an address, but apart from that she must be on her own, to try to adjust to all that had happened. She would have to use the money that Piran had put into a bank account for her, but that couldn't be helped. Money was the last thing she wanted to think about.

Joe was looking at his watch and shaking his head doubtfully. 'There's only the one train now, Mrs St Just, and that's lateish. You'd not get into London until about half-past three in the morning. I'm sure Mr St Just wouldn't like you to be about at that time on your own.'

Polly said in a tight little voice, 'Mr St Just wouldn't care where I was.' She heard Mrs Joe's gasp and went on, 'You must have noticed, Mrs Joe, that things weren't right between us. We're—we're splitting up now, and—oh, please, both of you, help me to get away tonight,' she finished desperately.

A glance passed between the two on the sofa. Then Joe nodded slowly, 'If that's what you want, Mrs St Just, I'll drive you into Wareham and see you on the train.'

CHAPTER NINE

POLLY sat in the swaying, jolting railway carriage that was taking her further and further away from Piran every moment and looked out at black, empty windows that reflected a face that she hardly recognised as her own. It was pinched and white— ghastly white—and her hair was flat and straggling against the collar of the light coat which was all she had brought with her to cover the thin wool dress she was wearing when Piran had delivered his ultimatum.

Why had everything gone so desperately wrong? She tried to search her tired brain for an answer. *Had* it been her fault, as he had cruelly thrown at her, for expecting too much of the marriage—more than he had offered?

Had it been her fault that she had fallen in love? Could that ever be called a fault? Polly leaned forward, elbows on knees, burying her face in her hands, and the bewhiskered elderly gentleman at the other end of the seat spoke for the first time on the journey. 'Are you feeling quite well, young lady? You don't look very good.'

Polly lifted her head. 'Thank you—I'm not ill, just very tired.' She was grateful for his presence in the carriage. From further down the carriage came the sound of raucous singing and the clatter of beer cans. Polly had noticed the young men come in at Bournemouth and guessed that they were students, probably from one of the language schools. But the elderly gentleman looked like a retired Army man and she was sure that he could deal promptly with the riotous brigade if they became embarrassing to her.

He smiled behind his moustache. 'Why not have a sleep, then? I'll keep the hordes at bay.' He indicated the noise coming from further down the carriage. He looked at his watch. 'You're going on to London? We don't get in until some unearthly hour, so have a good rest.'

Polly murmured, 'Thank you,' and closed her eyes, but she had never been further from sleep. Her head felt as if it were full of buzzing insects. Where would she go? What would she do? She would have to try and find a hotel, but what hotel would take her in in the middle of the night?

She wouldn't go to Alice, though. Alice would be kind and sympathetic, but Polly knew that kindness would destroy her at this moment. She would give in and that mustn't happen. She was on her own. Completely on her own, and that was how it was going to be for a long time. Perhaps for ever. She couldn't imagine any man taking Piran's place in her heart.

And he didn't love her—didn't even want her to stay. The bitterness of rejection worked its way coldly through her, touching every part of her, eating into her very soul, leaving her like a spent firework, lying somewhere in a gutter, all the life burned out of it.

And there was something else too, something that she couldn't face yet. A possibility—growing to a probability over the last two weeks—and now almost a certainty. She thrust the thought away; she only knew she couldn't run to Piran for protection if she was going to have his child.

The train rumbled on and on endlessly through the darkness, stopping for interminable spells, and then clanking into motion again. The elderly gentleman unscrewed the plastic cup from a flask of coffee and insisted on Polly drinking some. She was grateful for the hot, sweet liquid, but she still could not control the shivering inside.

Then at last, when she had almost begun to believe they would never arrive, they were there, grinding slowly into Waterloo Station, jolting to a stop.

There were only a few passengers getting out. The elderly gentleman helped Polly down the steep step with a gallant gesture, and she walked stiffly beside him along the cold, almost deserted platform. The students were jostling each other along in front, keeping up the noise to the end. Their voices echoed through the huge empty station.

At the barrier the elderly gentleman paused, looking down at Polly a trifle worriedly. 'You'll be all right, young lady? You're being met? I wouldn't like my own daughter to——'

'Oh yes, I'll be quite all right, please don't bother about me.' Polly spoke hastily, urgently. He was kind, but she didn't want him, she didn't want anyone. She was terrified that she would break down, and if she did start to cry she didn't know when she would stop. It was a tremendous physical effort to hold back the tears.

'Well, if you're sure——' he still hesitated uncertainly. And then, raising his hat courteously, 'I'll wish you goodnight, then.' He moved away towards the exit.

For a moment Polly stood quite still, made helpless by the sudden tears that blinded her. She squeezed her eyelids together, willing the tears to stop, biting her lower lip until she tasted blood, her fingers stiffly gripping the handle of her travelling case. A small, unhappy, lost figure in the chilly expanse of the station forecourt.

Then her eyes flew open in sudden alarm as the sound of running feet echoed through the empty area.

She saw the figure of a man tearing across the forecourt in her direction and her first frightened thought was, It's a chase—someone escaping from the police. But there didn't seem to be anyone chasing him. He was still coming straight towards her and she stumbled back out of his line of approach, but he changed direction and a moment later she was caught in a powerful grip. There was a moment of icy, confused terror, and then Piran's voice, breathing jerkily, came in her ear. 'Hallelujah! I made it. Next time the Le Mans Road Race!'

It couldn't be true—she was dreaming. She opened her eyes and over Piran's shoulder saw the elderly gentleman standing at the exit, looking very hard in her direction. He must think she had been attacked by a maniac. She lifted a hand and waved to him in reassurance, and he waved back before he turned and walked on.

Piran loosed her and followed the direction of her glance. 'Who's your friend?' he growled.

Suddenly Polly bubbled over. He had come after her—he hadn't let her go. Never mind why, never mind if it was still just for Jules's sake. He was here beside her, unbelievably, magically, wonderfully. 'An Army type,' she said gaily. 'An absolute sweetie! We travelled together.'

'Oh, you did, did you? I hope you didn't arrange to meet again because if you did he's going to be disappointed.' His arm held her as if he was afraid she would dart away from him at any moment. 'Come along, my car's outside. I shouldn't be surprised if the tyres are burned up. I've never driven so far in such a short time in my life, and that's saying something!'

He hustled her out to his car and pushed her inside. Polly relaxed into the soft leather of the seat with a long, long sigh. Piran was silent as he drove out of the station and into the London streets, never quite empty of traffic, but almost empty at four o'clock in the morning. A few minutes later the car stopped outside a tall old house in a square.

'Come along,' said Piran, and yanked Polly out unceremoniously.

He rang a bell and a large man in trousers and a thick pullover opened the door. 'Hullo, Mr St Just, glad you managed to get here. And your wife.' He gave Polly a wide grin. 'Number eight's ready for you, and I've put a bottle of your favourite in there and some sandwiches and biscuits. O.K.?'

'Splendid, Reggie, you're a pal. We'll go right up and let you get some sleep. Thanks for waiting up.'

The big man chuckled as a note changed hands. 'Always pleased to oblige, Mr St Just.'

Piran tucked an arm through Polly's, his other hand carrying her case. 'Number eight's on the second floor, I'm afraid, and the lift goes off at midnight. Do you feel strong enough to walk, or shall I carry you?'

Polly giggled. She felt lightheaded, as if she had drunk champagne. 'I'll do my best.'

Number eight was a spacious room, furnished for comfort rather than show. A writing desk, a side table, deep chairs, a positively enormous double bed. Polly looked away from that quickly and sank into a chair; Piran took the chair beside her and proceeded to open the bottle of wine that had been placed on the low table between them, together with a plate of wrapped sandwiches. 'Drink that up,' Piran ordered, handing her a glass. 'You look as if you need it.'

'All right, so I look a wreck,' said Polly, wrinkling her nose at him. 'You needn't rub it in.' It was extraordinary, the way she felt, as if she could say anything at all to Piran now. It was as if everything had changed between them, because he had come after her, even although she didn't yet know exactly why.

Jules—of course! She said sharply, 'What about Jules? You haven't left him on his own?'

He moved his shoulders impatiently. 'To hell with Jules—it's you I've been thinking about.'

Her eyes flew open wide in amazement. Never had she expected to hear him say that. He saw her expression and grinned faintly. 'No, of course I didn't leave him. Mrs Joe promised to go up and stay with him until we get home. And that won't be until tomorrow. I couldn't face a drive back tonight, even if you could.'

Until we get home. He had said 'we'. 'You—you mean you want me to come back with you?'

'I want you to come back with me,' he said, and there was something in his voice that she had not heard there before—a deep, throbbing emotion.

He didn't move towards her, or try to touch her. He just sat quite still, gazing at her as if he couldn't believe that she was there beside him.

Then, still not moving, he said wonderingly, 'I love you, Polly. I'm fathoms deep in love with you. I never thought I should hear myself say that, but there it is, and I'm at your mercy.'

He passed a hand across his brow and she saw that it was damp. 'I know damn well,' he went on, 'that you're not in love with me—how could you be after the way I've treated you—used you——' his face darkened '—raped you. But if you'll give me time I truly believe I could make you forget all that. I believe I could persuade you to love me.'

Polly looked into his eyes, and what she saw there sent spasms of warm excitement trembling through her. Her blue eyes met his dark, pleading ones, and she said quietly, 'I was always taught that it was wicked to waste time. Don't you think we've already wasted enough?'

For a moment he seemed transfixed, incredulous. Then she reached out a hand and touched his knee, and the touch seemed to electrify him. With a whoop of joy he was on his feet, pulling her into his arms, straining her against him as if he needed to fuse their two bodies together.

His mouth came down to hers hard and demanding and her lips parted gladly to his probing mouth. For a long time they stood locked together, then she felt him begin to tremble against her.

'There's only one place for us now,' he muttered, and he lifted her in his arms and carried her to the big bed. He laid her down and stood for a moment looking down at her, his eyes glittering black under their heavy lids. 'You want it too, Polly, don't you?'

'Yes,' she sighed languorously. 'Oh yes!'

This was different from what had gone before. Not the gentle, soothing sensuousness of the night Polly had had her nightmare. Not the brutal plundering of her body that had happened when he had worked himself into an angry passion.

This time he was all dominant, confident male. With firm, loving hands he undressed her, peeling off the final flimsy garment with a sigh of delight as his eyes devoured the smooth paleness of her slender limbs, stretched out on the woven bedspread.

Then, with a couple of quick movements, he had stripped off his own clothes, turned back the covers and lifted her beneath them, before he began his arousing exploration of her body.

Polly's eyes closed as his hands and mouth moved over her, awaking some new delight every moment, until she moaned with an aching need, all the more potent for having been denied all these weeks.

'Polly, my darling, my darling girl——' The broken words came close to her ear as he buried his mouth in the hollow of her neck before the final, shattering culmination of their mutual love, and she heard her own cry of fulfilment before they both lay quiet, clinging together, flesh against flesh, heart pounding against heart, in the wide bed.

It was Piran who stirred first. 'Sleep, my sweetheart,' he murmured, easing them both until she lay moulded into the curve of his body, their heads close together on one pillow. 'Sleep now.'

Utterly blissful, Polly slept.

She wakened to light pouring in through uncurtained windows and a feeling that the whole world was shining new. She wriggled round to see Piran, propped on one elbow, looking down at her, smiling with such tenderness that her inside seemed to turn over slowly.

She smiled back at him, her mouth twitching with mischief. 'Would it be permitted to enquire exactly where we are? This isn't a hotel, is it?'

He shook his head. 'No, it's a small club, mostly patronised by writers. I've been a member for years and I often stay here when I don't want to impose on Alice, or when I know she's working on some important commission. Reggie, the caretaker, is a gem——ex-Naval. I managed to get through to him on the phone just before I left last night to warn him we were coming.'

Polly asked, 'What exactly *did* happen last night? It still seems like a dream to me.'

He reached out and stroked her bright hair. 'A good dream, I hope?'

'A wonderful dream,' she told him fervently. 'I thought, all the way to London, on that slow, beastly train, that I was quite alone again. I'd been trying to face it when——' she laughed shakily '—when you pounced on me in the station.'

He slid down beside her and wrapped his arms around her strongly. 'You'll never be alone again, my darling. Never so long as I'm alive.'

'But I don't really understand. You kept on saying you weren't in love with me and I thought——'

'I was trying to fool myself,' he cut in. 'I'd told myself I'd never risk giving my love to any woman again, and when I found myself getting out of my depth with you I overacted more than somewhat. All those days in Paris I was getting in deeper and deeper, but still I wouldn't admit it to myself. By the time we got home I was beginning to break out of that hard shell I'd built round myself. And then—when you moved your bedroom to get further away from me, I think I went a bit crazy. I'd been wrong about you all the time, I told myself, you didn't give two hoots for me, it was only Jules that you were interested in. After my—outrageous behaviour that night I really believed I'd lost you, and I told myself I was glad.'

He drew her a little closer and pressed his lean hard cheek against the soft curve of her breast. 'I even tried to find a kind of consolation elsewhere.'

'Esmée Clark?' said Polly.

He lifted his head quickly. 'You knew?'

'She called on me as soon as we arrived,' Polly told him. 'To collect her clothes and belongings—from your bedroom.'

Piran groaned. 'That was all before I even knew you existed, my sweet.'

'But afterwards—you found—er—consolation? She told me she had a cosy little cottage up the coast somewhere.'

'Does it matter to you?'

Polly shook her head thoughtfully. 'Not now. I was

screaming with jealousy at the time, though.'

'Jealousy? You *did* love me, then?'

'I did love you,' said Polly. 'I did. I do. I'm afraid I always shall. In spite of the Esmée Clarks of this world.'

He laughed shortly. 'O.K., I suppose I deserve that last crack,' he said. 'But for the record, she did *not* provide consolation—or anything else. I admit I intended to use poor Esmée as a kind of disinfectant that would wash you out of my mind and my heart for good. My God——' he pulled himself up and buried his head in his hands, '—what bloody fools we men can be! But when it came to the point she revolted me. I ran like a hare and spent the rest of the night wandering about the heath, thinking about you and feeling sorry for myself.' He took his hands away and looked down at her ruefully. 'Can you still love me, Polly, after all this self-indulgent outpouring?'

She reached up and pulled him down to her, winding her arms round his neck. 'Oh yes,' she said placidly, against his mouth. 'Quite easily.'

His lips against hers, he breathed, 'You know what you're doing to me, don't you?' And her reply seemed to satisfy him.

Hours later they drove home through a golden October evening. They had called in briefly to see Alice, who had looked into Polly's shining eyes when they had a moment alone, and whispered, 'I'm so very, very glad I was wrong,' and then waved them off cheerfully with the invitation to 'come back soon, and bring that delightful child Jules with you.'

'We will, we will!' they called as they drove away.

Piran drove the powerful car with a kind of controlled prudence, very different from the reckless driving that Polly had noticed on the last occasion they drove to his home. Gradually the darkness closed in and they seemed to be taking so long over the journey that at last she raised herself out of her rainbow dream to say, 'I do hope Mrs Joe hasn't been too inconvenienced, having Jules to look after.'

'She won't mind,' Piran told her easily. 'She was delighted when she knew I was hot on your trail last night. If I'd come to my senses half an hour earlier I'd have caught you at the station before your train left. Would you have come back with me then, if I'd asked you?'

'Perhaps,' said Polly with a mischievous little grin, and he raised his hand from the wheel in mock threat.

After another mile or so Piran pulled into a layby and switched off the engine and the headlights. Outside the car the darkness was black velvet, enclosing them in a little world of their own, with only the dim reflection of the sidelights. He turned to her. 'There's just one more thing to clear up before we make a fresh beginning. Last night—I expect you thought I behaved like an absolute bastard when you arrived home with Aubrey. You see, I'd meant to stay overnight in London, after interviewing my publisher. But you were there all the time, I couldn't get you out of my mind. So eventually I decided to come back home and surprise you, possibly even to tell you I loved you, if I could get up enough courage. And when I got home the house was empty. Dark and empty—and you and Jules had gone. It seemed as if it was all happening again.' He ran a hand roughly through his hair in a desperate gesture. 'It was pure hell. I thought——'

Polly reached up and put a hand gently over his mouth. 'Don't say it,' she said. 'Don't say any more. I know—Alice told me what happened before. I'll always remember that, and try to understand.'

His arm went out and drew her near and he buried his cheek in her soft hair. 'Polly, my darling,' he said huskily, 'you're a lovely, kind, wonderful girl and I adore you. You deserve the very best. I want us to start all over again without any ghosts. I want us to have a real home and a real family. I want to make a good life for us and I swear I will—can you believe me?'

'I believe you,' she said. She turned her head and they kissed slowly, almost solemnly, as if they were making their vows all over again.

They drew apart and for a long moment looked into each other's eyes in silence. Then, 'Home now!' Piran cried exultantly, and switched on the engine and the headlights and a white beam shone out along the road ahead.

The powerful car purred steadily on through the darkness, and as it went a different scene arose vividly before Polly's eyes.

There was a long, sloping lawn bordered with trees and at the end of it a green hill rose against the sky. Clusters of sheep were dotted here and there, like grey toys in the distance. Smoke from a farmhouse chimney plumed into the still air, and beyond that the sea glinted deep blue under a summer sun. On the lawn, under the big apple tree, there was a pram with a linen canopy, and there was a small boy sitting on the grass beside it, his dark head bent over a book. Polly sighed as the picture faded and looked up at the strong profile of her husband etched against the darkness.

Her eyes misted with love and compassion and trust in the future. 'I'll tell him tomorrow,' she promised herself happily.

ROMANCE

Variety is the spice of romance

Each month, Mills & Boon publish new romances. New stories about people falling in love. A world of variety in romance – from the best writers in the romantic world. Choose from these titles in April.

AN ELUSIVE DESIRE Anne Mather
SUP WITH THE DEVIL Sara Craven
ONE WHO KISSES Marjorie Lewty
ONE MORE TIME Karen van der Zee
A MOUNTAIN FOR LUENDA Essie Summers
PHANTOM MARRIAGE Penny Jordan
CAPTIVE LOVING Carole Mortimer
MASTER OF MORLEY Kay Thorpe
SOMEWHERE TO CALL HOME Kerry Allyne
DARK SEDUCTION Flora Kidd
SECOND TIME AROUND Elizabeth Oldfield
THE TYCOON'S LADY Kay Clifford

On sale where you buy paperbacks. If you require further information or have any difficulty obtaining them, write to: Mills & Boon Reader Service, PO Box 236, Thornton Road, Croydon, Surrey CR9 3RU, England.

Mills & Boon
the rose of romance

ROMANCE

Next month's romances from Mills & Boon

Each month, you can choose from a world of variety in romance with Mills & Boon. These are the new titles to look out for next month.

DESIRE'S CAPTIVE Penny Jordan
FEVER PITCH Sarah Holland
CANDLEGLOW Amii Lorin
THE MARRIAGE CONTRACT Susan Alexander
CLOSEST PLACE TO HEAVEN Lynsey Stevens
DREAM OF MIDSUMMER Catherine George
MOMENT OF MADNESS Patricia Lake
LIONS WALK ALONE Susanna Firth
FANTASY GIRL Carole Mortimer
STORMY WEATHER Sandra Clark
INTIMATE ENEMIES Jessica Steele
THE SLENDER THREAD Yvonne Whittal

Buy them from your usual paperback stockist, or write to: Mills & Boon Reader Service, P.O. Box 236, Thornton Rd, Croydon, Surrey CR9 3RU, England. Readers in South Africa-write to: Mills & Boon Reader Service of Southern Africa, Private Bag X3010, Randburg, 2125.

Mills & Boon
the rose of romance

Advocates for Hinterland:
Nathan Hamilton, Kathryn Hughes, Helen Smith, Rebecca Stott,
Ian Thomson

Editorial Team
Editors-In-Chief – Yin F. Lim & Andrew Kenrick
Art Direction & Design – Tom Hutchings
Business Support – Ben Watkins
Copyeditor – Susan K Burton
Proofreaders – Finn Brocklesby, Susan K. Burton, Sophie Clarke,
      Vicki Leigh, Stephen Massil, Yashika Mathur,
      Florence Pearce-Higginson and Yianni Theochari
Founding Editors – Freya Dean & Andrew Kenrick

Submissions
Hinterland is committed to paying writers and artists for all work we publish.
Please send us your work via Submittable:
hinterlandnonfiction.submittable.com
We accept submissions year-round and endeavour to reply within 4 months.
We regret we are unable to provide feedback.
There is a small fee of £3 per submission.

Subscriptions
An annual subscription to Hinterland (four issues, print and digital)
costs £40 U.K., £44 Europe, £54 Rest-of-world.
Digital subscription only, £20. Please visit our website for full details.

Distribution
Hinterland is distributed worldwide by NBN International.
For all trade orders contact +44 (0) 1752 202301
orders@nbninternational.com

Advertising
Please see our website for current rates, or to discuss sponsorship please
contact us at hinterlandnonfiction@gmail.com

Acknowledgments
The Editors gratefully acknowledge financial contributions from
the UEA Publishing Project and the National Centre for Writing.

Find Hinterland online at
www.hinterlandnonfiction.com
or contact us: hinterlandnonfiction@gmail.com

ISBN: 978-1-913861-91-9
ISSN (Print): 2632-136X
ISSN (Online): 2632-1378

HINTERLAND

THE BEST NEW CREATIVE NON-FICTION

Issue 12
2022

Issue 12

Contributors

Munizha Ahmad-Cooke (*The Right Thing*) currently works as a charity administrator and freelance copyeditor. She grew up in Harrow, north-west London, and has lived in Cambridge since 2005. She has published some poems, book reviews and articles, and has worked in academia, publishing, politics and the charity sector. She recently co-edited *Edgewords*, an anthology of creative writing to raise money for The Edge Café in Cambridge.

Laura Dobson (*How To Care for a Rose*) lives in Devon where she is currently completing an MSc in Psychology. She is the proud owner of almost forty thriving houseplants and relishes sharing the therapeutic potential of creativity with young people. She has recent work in *Ellipsis Zine, WestWord, The Phare Literary Magazine* and *The Birdseed Magazine*. She can be found on Twitter @laurarose_13.

Edvige Giunta (*Wanna Dance?*) was born in Sicily and lives in the United States. She is the author of *Writing with an Accent: Contemporary Italian American Women Authors* and co-editor of six anthologies, including *The Milk of Almonds: Italian American Women Writers on Food and Culture*, and *Talking to the Girls: Intimate and Political Essays on the Triangle Shirtwaist Factory Fire*. Her most recent writing appears in *December Magazine, Pithead Chapel, Paris Lit Up, Ocean State* Review and *Memoir Magazine*, among others. She is Professor of English at New Jersey City University. www.edvigegiunta.com.

Candice Kelsey (*Failure to Stop*) [she/her] is a poet, educator and activist in Georgia. She serves as a creative writing mentor with PEN America's Prison Writing Program. Her work appears in *Grub Street, Poet Lore, Lumiere Review, Hawai'i Pacific Review* and *The Worcester Review* among other journals. Recently, Candice was chosen as a finalist in *Iowa Review's* Poetry Contest and her third book titled *A Poet* just released. She loves 80s detective shows, Puccini and dismantling fatphobia. Find her @candicekelsey1 & candicemkelseypoet.com.

Tom Hutchings is our in-house graphic designer, and this issue he is taking writing his blurb very seriously despite his daughter's best efforts. He has over a decade of experience in design, layout and photography, working across print, film and games. As a freelance designer he loves to find joy and playfulness in his work, and as such is very excited for the snow and holidays. You can find his work at thorngraphicdesign.com

Lim Siang Jin (*Fear and Hope in Covid Times*) is a self-taught artist who has been painting since the mid-1970s. At 69, he has had three excursions into art: years at university in Britain as a student and as a rookie journalist in Malaysia (1973-1982); time he spent at a Malaysian policy research institute as head of publications (1985-1991); and during and after the Covid lockdowns (2020-2022). There was a gap of 30 years (1989-2020) when he hardly produced anything new. During much of the three decades, he was deeply involved in newspaper publishing, communications, and branding and marketing.

Jarred McGinnis (*In Billions of Years the Sun will Swallow the Earth*) was chosen by *The Guardian* as one of the UK's ten best emerging writers. His debut novel *The Coward* was selected for BBC 2's Between the Covers, BBC Radio 2's Book Club and listed for the Barbellion Prize. The French edition won the First Novel Prize and was selected for the prestigious Femina prize. His current project *The Mountain Weight* won the 2023 The Eccles Centre & Hay Festival Writer's Award.

Joe Moran (*Noli Timere*) is a Professor of English and Cultural History at Liverpool John Moores University. His books include *Shrinking Violets: The Secret Life of Shyness* (Profile/Yale University Press, 2016/2017), *First You Write a Sentence: The Elements of Reading, Writing ... and Life* (Penguin, 2018) and *If You Should Fail: A Book of Solace* (Penguin, 2020).

Elizabeth Norton (*We Circle Silently About the Wreck*) is a writer living in London. She is currently completing her creative writing MA at Birkbeck and is working on her first novel. She works in the criminal justice sector.

Ali Seegar (*And Who Would I Then Have Been?*) writes fiction, non-fiction and poetry for all age groups. Publications include her children's book series, 'Tommy Turner's Travels'. In 2022 she won the London Independent Story Prize with her short story *Nothing Happens Until Something Moves*. Ali started her professional life as a dancer until a knee injury forced her to stop. She now lives in Luxembourg, where she regularly visits schools and libraries to give creative writing workshops, and has recently graduated from the University of Oxford's Creative Writing diploma with distinction. She is currently working on the first book of a YA fantasy series.

Richard Skelton
(*Apparitions, Dust*) is an artist from northern England. His work – writing, music, artworks, films – is rooted in the particularities of specific landscapes, from the moors of Lancashire to the fells of Cumbria, the karst hills of western Ireland to the fjords of eastern Iceland. He is co-director, with the Canadian poet Autumn Richardson, of Corbel Stone Press, one of the foremost British small presses dedicated to publishing work that is focused on landscape and the natural world. For the past half-decade he has lived on the rural border of Scotland and England.

Michelle Spinei (*The Conversationalist*) is an American writer based in Reykjavík. Her work has been featured in *Catapult*, *Ós Pressan* and *Fodor's*.

Adrian Tissier (*Travellers over the Fields*) is a writer and performer, currently studying for an MA in Creative Non-Fiction at UEA. He has delivered creative writing workshops and performed award-winning storytelling and poetry events at the Manchester Literature Festival and Buxton Festival Fringe. Previously he worked for the National Trust, specialising in delivering workshops and training for environmental interpretation and inspiring immersive experience, and has presented at conferences nationally and internationally. He is also a trained teacher of English and drama, and has written books on poetry and English language for Longman Literature. Instagram: @tissieradrian

Raised in South London, **Dave Wakely** (*Eating Cornflakes with Patrick Moore*) has worked as a musician, university administrator, poetry librarian and editor in cities across Europe. His short stories and poems have been shortlisted for the Manchester Fiction and Bath Short Story awards, and appeared in numerous journals and anthologies, including most recently *Impossible Archetypes, The Lonely Crowd, Lunate, Prole* and *We're All In It Together: Poems for a disUnited Kingdom* (Grist Books). One of the organisers of the Lodestone Poets and Milton Keynes Literature Festival, he lives in Buckinghamshire with his husband and too many books, CDs and guitars. He tweets as @theverbalist.

Sam Gordon Webb (*Unsung*) is a writer studying Crime Fiction at UEA. His writing has appeared in *Beyond Words,* and *Unstamatic.* He is social media coordinator for *Chestnut Review,* and *Leapfrog Global Fiction Prize* project manager. He is working on his debut novel as a student of Faber Academy's Writing a Novel course. Champion of cappuccinos and blueberry muffins. He can be found @samofme.

Editorial

The global pandemic we've experienced in recent years has left many of us with a greater preoccupation with the body, prompting much contemplation around sickness and health, life and death. Matters of the body however, encompass many varied areas of our lives. This is particularly evident with many of the authors who are 'writing the body' in this issue.

Bodies can be afflicted and affected in many different ways. Munizha Ahmad-Cooke shows what it's like to live with a loved one's addiction and its impact on relationships, while Dave Wakely's unconventional account of a family member's decline casts a horrible illness as a pantomime villain. In Laura Dobson's hermit crab essay, the spectre of an old eating disorder is never far as an undergraduate completes her Fashion Design degree.

The extreme limits to which we can push our bodies are explored in Elizabeth Norton's fragmentary account of freediving and the submersion of female bodies in 'deep bodies of water', while Edvige Giunta's coming-of-age tale sees a burgeoning awareness of the body in desire as captured in a love triangle.

Yin F Lim spent many years as a journalist writing other people's stories before deciding to write her own. She completed a Creative Non-Fiction MA at the University of East Anglia and now mainly writes about family, food and migration.

The body can also be represented in birth and our sense of self, as seen in Jarred McGinnis' parental rumination of his time travel through the life of his daughter, as well as Ali Seegar's reflections about who she might have been had the circumstances around her adoption been different.

Coming full circle we, inevitably, arrive at the end of life. Inspired by the death of a dear friend during the Covid pandemic, Joe Moran examines grief as experienced through the disembodied voices and digital ghosts of our online lives. Mortality is also at the fore of Richard Skelton's mythogeographic remembering of his own private 'Isle of the Dead' as seen through art and literature, including Arnold Böcklin's painting of the same name.

Together with flash non-fiction ranging from an exploration at the intersection of chance, fate, and free will to a vignette of an unpleasant dinner guest, we hope we've curated an issue that entertains as much as it provokes thought and discussion.

The Editors

Andrew Kenrick has worked as an archaeologist and an archivist, a writer and an editor. He is currently studying for a PhD at the University of East Anglia, where he also teaches English Literature and Publishing.

Failure to Stop

by Candice Kelsey

KELSEY BALISH, 51, mother, wife, poet, works
as a high school English teacher, battles depression
and anxiety, working through mild PTSD from
the sexual harassment she endured at a previous
school, handles all her family's finances, tumultuous
marriage, most recent fight centered around the
new Beatles documentary, *Get Back*, elected to stay
home alone under the guise of self-care rather
than go with her three children to her husband's
basketball tournament three hours away, secretly
bites her tongue until it bleeds.

ALLIE MAE BALISH, 19, oldest daughter,
sophomore in college, fiercely independent, struggles
with ADHD and intrusive thoughts, plucks strands
of her hair when anxious, recently began vaping
and occasionally abuses her Adderall, tired and a
bit resentful of her parents' arguments, but happily
willing to drive her younger siblings to her father's
basketball tournament three hours away, always
carries a bottle of Tabasco on her person.

TOTALED HONDA FIT, 2014, 68,000 miles
with a purple college decal on the rear window and
empty bottles of Adderall and Tabasco in the glove
compartment.

JAKEY BALISH, 15, middle child, only son, just withdrew from a military academy after one semester, consumed with weightlifting and baseball, breaking in his new first baseman's glove.

CORDELIA BALISH, 13, youngest child and daughter, given to emotional outbursts, in the throes of puberty, recently began meditating in the mornings, happy to have her brother and sister home.

MARLENE BALISH, 10, female cousin, related to the BALISHES on her father's side, lives in Nashville, parents are embroiled in a bitter divorce, father and older sisters are on this trip too.

NANNY'S GHOST, ageless, late paternal grandmother of the BALISH children and mother-in-law of KELSEY, passed away eleven years ago from ovarian cancer; the family has never recovered. Attempted to play the role of protecting angel, saving grace, supernatural guardian to no avail.

DUCK HUNTERS, ubiquitous in the early mornings by the Savannah River, buckshot often attracting shouts of 'Stop!' from KELSEY.

FOUR WHITE CROSSES, 18 inches tall, wooden, planted near enough to be almost touching. No one has left flowers.

SHERIFF AMOS TUPPER, fictional lawman
of the 80s TV show *Murder, She Wrote*, airing on
Amazon Prime Video, paused on a close-up of his
perplexed expression in KELSEY's living room as
she answers the phone and hears of the accident. ◙

Travellers over the fields

by Adrian Tissier

14th February, Sheffield
The snow in the night, as so often happens, fell
at first as a soft and delicate powder, scarcely
noticeable; floating flakes. A romantic sight
for Valentine's Day. But this soft, white silence
continued for hour after hour. A gentle killer. Now
cars float quietly, ghost-like, past the house. The
back garden is hushed as the outlines of tree and
hedge have been transformed, branches striped
in black and white lines; fairy kingdoms outlined
against bright blue sky.

The morning air is very still and my footsteps
break the silence with a creaking crunch. The bird
song that was gathering in intensity a few days
earlier has been silenced.

The thin 'tseep' of a great tit wavers.

Birds have left the woods. They are sheltering
in the hedges, seemingly lining every branch.
Movement and sound begin. A pair of wrens and
a pair of blue tits creep and flit through the privet.
The hawthorn buzzes with starlings and scolding
flurries of blackbirds that fuss and flutter. Then
a winter cloud of wings appears out of the sky,
the flock attracted by the crimson beads of the
cotoneaster berries.

Fieldfares. Forced to overcome their natural,
wild aloofness.

The usual view of these winter thrushes is a distant one, as they rove across the open fields and hills following the daily changes in weather, to seek out food and shelter. But now the birds are close up and immediate in the back garden, these larger and more forceful relatives of our native blackbird and song thrush. I see flashes of their colour in the snow; slate grey, chestnut, and cream. As they squabble for berries they utter throaty 'clacking' and chattering calls as if they are on the verge of getting angry with whatever or whoever stands in their way.

As I clear away great mounds of snow from the small patch of lawn, scattering an assortment of nuts, seeds and fruit, I feel a hundred pairs of eyes watching me intently from every available perch. By the time I break the ice on the bird bath, the scramble for food has already started. Seventeen different species of birds visit the garden, not more than 100 metres away from one of the main roads into the heart of the city. Four species of finch, three species of tit, five thrushes, robin, dunnock, wren, house sparrow and starling.

A pair of bullfinches glow brightly against the snow, the male uttering his melancholy 'peep, peep' call, like a steady melting drip. Eighteen species and counting.

But it is the fieldfares that hold my attention, the 'frosty feldefares' as Chaucer calls them in *The Parliament of Fowls*, his poem heralding the coming of spring and celebrating Valentine's Day love. Derived from the Anglo-Saxon, 'felde-fare' literally means 'traveller over the fields', capturing a wild and poetic quality about these birds. In Irish the bird is called 'sacán' or the frost bird, another appropriate name as fieldfares often appear just before a change in the weather. I love the way John Clare, the great nature poet of the nineteenth century, captured the bird's affinity with winter in the lines,

'Flocking fieldfares, speckled like the thrush
Picking the red haw from the sweeping bush
That come and go on winter's chilling wing,
And seem to share no sympathy with Spring'

I also like how the Polish poet, Julian Kornhauser, gives the bird's arrival a more mysterious and perhaps darker quality,

'like a newcomer from the underworld'.

For me the fieldfare is the ultimate bird of winter. I remember as a schoolboy wistfully looking at them fly off from the playing fields as we ran out shivering on to the icy turf to play rugby. I wished I could follow them, away on their white, flashing wings over the fields, instead of having to spend the next hour being tackled in the frozen mud. Each year when I see the fieldfares return, I feel their nervous excitement as they gather in the treetops. In my imagination they carry with them on their wings the wild scent of Siberia and northern Scandinavia from where they have flown. There is a restless urgency about their movements and an otherworldliness in their chattering calls.

In his Afterword to *The Poetry of Birds*, Simon Armitage talks about their poetic relationship when he writes: 'Perhaps at some subconscious, secular level [birds] are also our souls. Or more likely, they are our poems. What we find in them we would hope for our work – that sense of soaring otherness. Maybe that's how poets think of birds: as poems.'

Fieldfares have that quality of 'soaring otherness' when they descend out of the snow-clouds into the trees, their heads all pointing the same way to catch the language of the wind currents. They take me to another place. I am climbing the hawthorn tree in our garden as a seven-year-old. I am watching a sea eagle sailing over the cliffs of Orkney. I am camping out at night under the stars.

Weighing just a hundred grams, the fieldfare flies every autumn two thousand miles or more through cold, night skies to reach a safe winter home, where it can find food and shelter. I think of the fieldfare as a symbol of resilience, and perhaps it carries also in its winter wanderings another message; that of its relationship to the land. It is a relationship not defined by ownership, but by an inter-connectivity with place. The fieldfare always adapts to the balance of available resources, as it feeds and moves on, allowing the earth to recover. The holly and rowan berries it eats are part of a sustainable, ecological process, the fruit being provided by the trees in return for the seeds being dispersed by the birds.

If, as Armitage says, 'birds are our souls', then perhaps we need to listen more deeply to the fieldfare's message in our soul as they restlessly travel over the land. ◨

The Conversationalist

by Michelle Spinei

As soon as she sat down, I knew where the conversation was heading, or rather, where it was not heading. Perhaps it was the way she descended into her chair: back erect from a lifetime of Pilates classes that trained her to assume that a thread drawn from the base of her spine up to the top of her head elevated her from the rest. Or perhaps it was the way her gaze fell upon the most famous person at the table. Her torso turned by instinct, daisy to sun, and she directed her question as if there were only two.

She immediately got to work throwing out highly recognizable names in quick succession like the contents of an upturned bag of Italian leather. If she was famous, I wasn't aware and didn't have the opportunity to ask. I've never been a great conversationalist.

The discussion followed where she steered it:

'Don't you find Marilynne Robinson to be overrated?'

'Of course Hugh Jackman is amazing, but *The Music Man* was uneven and traditional. So passé.'

'Well I was one of the first people to see *Hamilton*...'
It was as if she had experienced a lifetime of being in the shadow of adoration. That she draped herself with importance, rubbed her scent into bold-faced names with a feverishness of ownership.

During a lull, one dinner guest tried to change the direction of the conversation, dared to assert himself. She intercepted and deftly changed the subject back to the most recent play she had attended. I took a bite of my bloody steak and gave him a sympathetic look. I would normally be annoyed with such behavior. A few years ago I might have labeled her insufferable, but either I had changed or the times had changed because I couldn't bring myself to judge her.

She was glowing. How wonderful it must have been for her that evening. After two years of solitude, to have an audience. After two years when culture stopped, Broadway shows canceled, museums closed, travel paused, events postponed, to have a reason to speak. To exist. After two years of being a phantom plus one. How had she survived?

I examined her out of curiosity, looking for signs of struggle. Her hair was newly dyed, no grays in sight. The overhead lighting highlighted delicate gold jewelry, tastefully chosen. Her clothing was understated and expensive in a warm taupe color; the one in which people in her circle love dressing themselves and painting every wall of their home. Not brown, not quite gray. It always reminded me of high-end patio furniture. Even her jet lag wasn't showing.

While she dominated the table and introduced her sentences with 'my husband and I', the stories she shared contained so little of what she had accomplished. I wondered if she had ever been an artist, and if she stored her dreams like a fur coat in a cold storage vault, when the kids and the committee responsibilities took over.

I once had a job that brought me in close proximity to women like her, with the houses and the nannies and the country clubs and the husbands or trust funds backing it all. I had to bring mail trays filled with thousands of invitations, kept in alphabetical order, to a mansion where women wrote notes encouraging their friends to attend an event with them.

I didn't know who owned the house, only the address and instructions on when to arrive and what to do. I wasn't there to make conversation. The women filtered in throughout the day and handed me stacks of notes with post-its affixed to each one that I filed into the correct envelope; a display of organized guilt tripping.

The house, decorated in bright white, was empty except for staff who filtered in and out of the kitchen, discreet and silent. I took a break and went to the bathroom. The walls were half-covered in large mercury glass tiles, a scented candle perfumed the air, and the toilet paper I reached for was monogrammed. There was something unseemly, too intimate, about wiping with the family initials and I resented that the paper refused to respect the distance I tried to create between myself and this environment. I dried my hands on my pants instead of the linen-paper guest towels, also personalized, denying myself the single-use luxury. What was with this insistence on stamping existence onto disposable products and why did it bother me?

When faced with death some of us acquiesce, some of us fall apart, and some of us hold on so tightly, marking every place with our initials like a compulsion left over from a childhood of carving our names into trees. We exist, we assert; look at us, we exist. I now live in a country where nature is ready to kill at any moment and each person is like a pixel in a vast landscape. You exist, nature asserts, and I don't care if you exist. It's healthy, reassuring even, to live in a place that does not assume itself to be the center of everything, to live among people who don't mistake the light fixture above for a spotlight.

I hadn't seen her kind in the wild since the world shut down. After years of so much tragedy and loss, how quickly the shallow and flippant grew back. Perhaps in her world they're still ordering monogrammed toilet paper; perhaps they never stopped. Something about it was reassuring, a brazen rebuttal against impermanence. Weeds often appear before the showy flowers of summer and I took her performance as a sign of hope, the bright purple crocus poking out of the snow.

She ordered a bottle of wine for the table and offered to pay when the bill arrived, but decided against it when it was suggested that the table split it. I wasn't surprised: big talkers are rarely big spenders. I paid my share happily and, thinking back, should have paid for hers as well, for she gave me more than she knew. **H**

Unsung

by Sam Gordon Webb

'Enjoy the rest of your life.'

The final words they speak. Imagine that. Imagine
the moment they enter the atmosphere, how it
feels in today's context: waiting lists; an 'explosion'
of demand in children's mental health services;
negligence; failure to act.

It screams in the silence. It stalks our country.

The news of their death in a ninety-eight-word
WhatsApp message hits me hard. Brevity isn't
always the soul of wit. It can also be the source of
grief, of loss, of agony.

'I'm not sure whether you know. I've only just found
out. Apparently, they died at the start of June.'

Sad face emoji.
Crying face emoji.
Angry face emoji.

I knew them. I knew them, even if we never truly
met. No trips to the beach; no evenings at the
bar; no rollercoasters; no ups and downs. Our
relationship was constructed by distance.

Looking back now, I arrive at the place where we first met.

I'm a nineteen-year-old patient at a psychiatric unit in South West London. I can see my ribcage, skin stretched, eyes burning, blood racing around my needle-thin flesh, every bone in my body aching, tingling. This is a pain that I feel, but do not accept. A reality that I know exists but keep at bay, push to the pits of life, feed to the wolves.

I have no awareness of pain. It's invisible to me, a hurrying air, a sensation; not the kind that people talk about in everyday life, no shapeless purple bruises to indicate the exact point of infliction. My pain is deep – too deep to see on a map, and erase – so it clasps to every ounce of my thoughts.

I needed to be told before I knew what I had. 'Atypical Anorexia Nervosa'. Life or death. Make or break. Choices they serve on a plate.

On the first night of my admission, I sit next to the senior nurse. The thin veil of her delicate smile hides the thickness of her concern, the occasional swallows, the conversations about the weather, the throat clearing, the clinking of knives and forks and the maneuvering of food on my plate. As if it isn't nourishment, but an intricate circuit board.

Fish pie, quarter portion, green beans dripping in lukewarm water, sitting at the 'beginners' table with struggling patients requiring tight observation. This is where I see them, our eyes meeting before anything else. Theirs are subtle, steeped in struggle. I can see this through their irises, not piercing, but disarming, like an instrument in a vast concert hall, playing alone, without backup. Stretched skin. A solemn tightness to the way they hold their arms on their belly.

They rarely speak, so when words fall from their mouth, they carry more weight. On this occasion, their lips, cracked and peeling, curl towards the broken fan above. 'Welcome to Avalon.' And the following moment, bleakness emerges from their gaze, their lips vibrating, lines forming on a peeling forehead, a rich red, a terrible sight if you look close enough, a bruise on their left cheek, faint purple and in the shape of a camel.

'Thank you', I say, taking a final mouthful of fish pie, a piece of salmon stuck between my two front teeth.

After dinner, they stay in their room, and even as we don't speak – preferring to keep ourselves to ourselves – our silence is a kind of melody. Or a better way of putting it: an *act of defiance*, closing off from chaos and drama, a soft beat of classical music playing through a radio speaker. Lying in bed, I listen to its muffled projection, imagining their eyes closed, their feet tingling in a stream of luscious inflections, each toenail dancing to the other. I imagine their humming, long and light; if it were a string, it would stretch far beyond the corridors of the ward into the concert halls again, wrapping itself around the room, a joyous hug.

Later, I discover that people have died here. The ward remains on a 'requires improvement' rating according to the latest reports. Poor care. Incorrect meal portions. Staff shouting at patients. Unhelpful and inexperienced. The list of failures runs deep. But their death is a new low for the NHS. Are we failing these people? Are we doing enough to prevent the loss of life?

As I gaze towards the darkening sky, I rejoice in the brief yet vibrant texture of their voice, sweet yet rare, like a mint chocolate. I bite into it, my teeth clenched, because if I swallow it quickly, it won't feel so awful when it's all gone, and perhaps the sweetness will cling to my tongue, my innards. ◧

'When a place has been altered beyond recognition and all hope seems lost, it might still hold the potential for life of another kind.'

- Cal Flyn

Cal Flyn is just one of the speakers in the RSL Spring season, to be announced January 2023.

RSL Membership
£60 a year

RSL Young Person's Membership
(for under 30s)
£40 a year

- Attend all of our **events** – over 25 each year – free of charge
- Bring a guest to each event at a discounted price of £5
- Subscribe free to our magazine *RSL Review*
- Attend our Summer Party and presentation of new Fellows
- Receive our **monthly e-newsletter**
- Take advantage of **exclusive offers** with our partner organisations
- Support our **charitable aims** as the UK's voice for the value of literature

Digital Events Pass
£25 a year
Attend all of our **online events** free of charge and enjoy a literary festival all year round, from wherever you are.

RSLiterature.org

32 Hinterland

Noli timere

by Joe Moran

On 13 November 2020, a leaving do was held at 10 Downing Street, in a room so crowded that people were perched on each other's laps. Later that evening, Abba's 'The Winner Takes It All' was heard coming from a party in the Prime Minister's flat. On 11 December, Number 10 took delivery of a new drinks fridge for the regular 'wine-time Fridays'. On 18 December, around fifty people attended a Christmas party, with cheese and wine and the exchange of Secret Santa gifts.

At the same time, my closest friend was dying. In those months, my only contact with her was a series of ever more desultory phone conversations, when she was either worn out and dreamy or high on steroids. At her funeral, in early February 2021, I was one of exactly thirty mourners. Everyone wore masks and no one hugged. At the end we briefly milled around outside, before the next thirty mourners from the next funeral came out. It was so cold that, when I looked down at my hands, I saw that my knuckles were bleeding.

When news of the lockdown parties broke, the most enraged were the bereaved – the ones who had been forced to say their farewells through windows in care homes or on iPads, or watch funerals on live streams on their laptops. Those defending the parties didn't understand, or pretended not to. *People had been working hard*, they said, *and we needed to maintain morale.*

—

Ever since our ancestors first sprinkled ochre on bodies 40,000 years ago, and buried them with favoured objects and adornments, we have needed rituals for the dying and the dead. Gathering round the bed to accompany those in their last hours on their voyage into the unknown, then cleansing and purifying the body, holding wakes, keening, eulogising, taking turns to shovel dirt into the grave, sitting shiva, breaking bread. The rituals wash over us and relieve us of the duty to think. They help to fill the void of unmeaning left when someone we love simply, shockingly, ceases to exist.

We share these rituals with other animals. One night in the summer of 1941, while watching a sett, the nature writer Brian Vesey-Fitzgerald saw a badger funeral. A sow and her son improvised a grave from an old rabbit's warren, dragged and heaved an older male into it, then roofed it with earth. The whole ceremony, throughout which they howled and whimpered and touched noses, lasted seven hours. The scientist and conservationist

Cynthia Moss, who has studied elephants in Kenya's Amboseli National Park since 1972, has seen them covering dead members of their herd with leaves and branches and standing vigil, then returning much later to stroke their bones; the Roman author Aelian observed the same elephant rituals in the third century. The animal behaviourist Marc Bekoff once witnessed the funeral of a magpie hit by a car. Four birds stood silently over the body, then flew off and brought back grass, twigs and pine needles to place beside it, like a wreath. After bowing their heads for a few seconds, they flew off.

Some scientists think that calling these things 'funerals' is just mushy anthropomorphism. You can observe animal behaviour, they say, but you can't prove what feelings lie behind it. The biologist E. O. Wilson noticed that when an ant dies, it lies ignored for two days. Then, when its body starts to release oleic acid, another ant carries it to a refuse pile of dead ants, the ant version of a graveyard. When Wilson applied oleic acid to a live ant's body and returned it to an ant trail, that ant was also carried off on another's back to the graveyard, struggling all the while.

I suppose a strict behaviourist would see the grieving rituals not just of ants but of all animals – perhaps even humans – like this, as a matter of chemical triggers and blind instinct. But I have seen a group of horses in a field with heads bowed over their dead comrade, and I know what I saw. Other animals can tell us something about why we have to say goodbye to those we have lost, even though we know it changes nothing. We need to be with our dying and our dead, and when we can't be, it feels as if a hole has been rent in the fabric of the universe.

We need to be with our dying and our dead, and when we can't be, it feels as if a hole has been rent in the fabric of the universe

For months after my friend's death, a line from a Paddy McAloon song, 'The Old Magician', kept popping into my head: *Death is a lousy disappearing act.* Things felt oddly dulled and affectless, as if the normal course of grief had stalled in the general surrealism of daily life in lockdown. Life went on, but laboriously. My brain felt like an old computer that more or less works, but takes ages to boot up and keeps freezing because of all the old programs and temporary files running in the background. It occurred to me that at some point the computer would stop working altogether, and those feelings, whirring away uselessly underneath, would have to be faced.

—

We owe to Sigmund Freud the now common idea of grief as an arduous road we must walk undeviatingly along. Bereaved people, he writes in his essay 'Mourning and melancholia', cleave so tightly to the memory of their lost beloved that 'a turning away from reality ensues'. Mourning demands *Trauerarbeit* or *grief work*: the hard labour of severing the ties that bind us to them. It means slowly conceding the truth that they are now, in Freud's unforgiving phrase, a 'non-existent object'.

I could hardly begin to think of my friend as not existing. For the last year of her life, I knew her the same way I knew almost everyone else – as a digital ghost, an incorporeal intelligence spirited through the air. And then, like a switch being tripped, she wasn't even that. How easy it was for me to believe that she had just mislaid her phone, the one with the scuffed Cath Kidston case, or forgotten to charge it. Or that she was somewhere with dodgy reception and was wandering around in the garden holding it up, trying to pick up a single bar of signal, and at any moment her thumbs would start dancing on its little screen, she would press send and her name would pop up again on my phone. *Sorry for the radio silence*, she would say – as people always say.

How easy it was for me to believe that she had just mislaid her phone... or forgotten to charge it

Even now, I still think an email might arrive with a friendly ping, and it will be her. Or that one of those little grunts when my phone shudders on silent might be her sending a text. Or that she might chip in to our WhatsApp group in the way that long-time lurkers suddenly and weirdly have something to say, and remind us with a jolt that they exist.

To Dr Freud, all this is just denial. *Must do better with your grief work*, he would say. *See me after class.*

———

Things carry on existing even when we can no longer see or hear them. We aren't born with this knowledge; we need to learn it. The psychologist Jean Piaget gave the name 'object permanence' to this awareness that a thing might live on even when it is absent to us. Piaget observed the reactions of infants when their favourite toy was covered with a blanket. Babies think the toy has gone for good. They seem briefly puzzled or sad, but then quickly give up on it. From around eight months old, though, they start to realise that the toy is just hidden. This newfound knowledge overlaps with the first wave of separation anxiety. Once a child grasps object permanence, the world becomes a more complicated and scarier place. The child knows when someone isn't there, but doesn't know when, or if, they will return. A parent in the next room might as well be on the moon.

Infants develop ways of coping with separation anxiety. In September 1915, Freud was staying at his daughter Sophie's house in Hamburg and was watching his 18-month-old grandson, Ernst, play a game of his own invention. Ernst would throw a wooden reel with a piece of string coiled around it out of his cot, exclaiming 'Oo!'. When he yanked on the string to bring the reel back into view, he uttered a gleeful 'Ah!'. Freud heard these sounds as infantile approximations of the German *fort*, 'gone', and *da*, 'there'. In the *fort-da* game, Ernst was symbolically commuting an unhappy situation, in which he had no control over the presence of his mother, into a happy one in which he could call her up at will.

Later on, we learn a harder truth. Human objects are not, in fact, permanent, and sometimes they will leave, never to return.

—

Our modern faith is the quest for perfect connectivity. These days it is as near as the godless get to the promise of eternal life. When the telegraph and the telephone were invented, the Victorians saw them as the electrical equivalents of that then-voguish pseudo-science, telepathy. These inventions seemed to fulfil the same dream of contact with distant others. Our online world is the culmination of that dream. It offers up an antidote to the depressing laws of physics which say that a human body is time-limited and gravity-bound.

This faith is fuelled by the market's unquenchable hunger for harvestable data. The online world cannot conceive that anything could end. There will always be another update or notification, another drop in the self-replenishing drip feed of gossip and comment. All you need to do is keep scrolling, dragging down to refresh, searching for the dopamine hit, the virtual hug that comes from being liked and shared. The dead live on in their undeleted social media accounts, still flogging their CVs and freelance pitches, their holiday photos, their pictures of long-consumed meals about to be eaten, their thoughts on Brexit and vaccines and face masks and *Love Island*. Everything online feels ongoing, as if death were a temporary bandwidth problem. Online, we think that things will be solved by saying them, by declaring our feelings and having them validated. *Thank you for sharing*, we say, because saying anything is always preferable to saying nothing.

Online, we think that things will be solved by saying them, by declaring our feelings and having them validated

In the early days of the first lockdown, a Second World War veteran in a care home was filmed in tears after being given a cushion with his late wife's face on it. Thousands shared the film online. This man had been sleeping with a picture of his wife in a frame, so his carer, worried he might cut himself if the glass broke, had the cushion made. A kind thing to do, of course. But why did it need to be filmed so that the sight of him crying could go viral? A stranger's tears allow us to think that something has been fixed. Click on the link, feel the warm glow of empathy by proxy, have a little cry yourself and then go back to your own life. Online, shedding and witnessing tears is seen as healthy, cathartic and semi-compulsory. But since when were tears ever a guarantor of sincerity or depth of feeling? Often, what provokes them has nothing to do with whatever is really making us sad. The other day, I cried when I couldn't tear the cellophane off a box of tea bags.

In *Wonderworks*, Angus Fletcher explores the neuropsychology of grief. Almost all of us, he writes, feel that it's wrong to stop grieving and move on with the rest of our lives. At the heart of this feeling lies guilt. Guilt's function is to keep a check on our relationships with others and raise the alarm when rifts form. The death of a loved one scrambles this system. Our brains sense their absence and warn us to heal the rift. But how can we, when they are no longer there? This is why our ancestors created funeral rites, which offer gifts to the dead in the shape of words, music and formalised gesture. They help a little, but these rituals can also feel empty and, well, ritualistic. Their stock utterances and choreographed moves can never account for the infinite particularity, the limitless heterogeneity, of the person who has gone. And that person can no longer relieve our guilt by accepting the gift of remembrance anyway, and telling us not to worry.

Our brains sense their absence and warn us to heal the rift. But how can we, when they are no longer there?

In the middle of a pandemic, with death a grim statistic on the nightly news, I worried that the uniqueness of my friend, the stubbornly singular way she took up space in the world, was being lost in the weight of numbers. But I also disliked the idea of sharing her with strangers, of posting some online tribute that followers of ever-diminishing proximity to her could answer with comments, likes and emojis. Why should she have to fight for space in the jarring juxtapositions of a Twitter timeline, sandwiched between someone saying *I'm so fucking angry* and someone else saying *I've been promoted?* I didn't want her to become part of the noise.

We need time, Fletcher says, to move beyond the necessary bromides and expedient clichés of memorials. We have to acknowledge that the person we have lost has left behind a human-shaped hole moulded to their precise dimensions, one that nothing and no one else will fill. Our brains must slowly absorb this brain-melting paradox of being human — that set against the billions of other selves who have lived and died, a single life doesn't matter much, and yet it matters beyond words.

—

Grief today comes with a script, and the script says this: it will obliterate us and then, painfully, remake us. Its trauma will be worth withstanding because it will teach us something important about ourselves. Even grief, in other words, has been co-opted into the progress myths and redemptive arcs of the personal growth industry. But why should the worst pain of all be turned into an opportunity for self-improvement? *Whatever doesn't kill you makes you stronger,* they say — even though a moment's serious thought reveals this to be nonsense.

In *All the Lives We Ever Lived*, Katharine Smyth writes about the death of her father from bladder cancer at the age of 59. After this long-anticipated event, her days just felt 'vague and muffled' – not the required response in our culture of 'grief worship'. Smyth wonders if we overinvest in the idea that grief floors us and changes us for ever. Instead, in its tedium and monotony, it 'recalls to us our impotence, reminds us that our longing counts for nothing'.

The slightly shaming truth is that grief is an anticlimax. If this is grief work, I remember thinking in the weeks after my friend's death, then it is the dullest desk job imaginable. The schedule isn't onerous or stressful; I seem to spend most of my time clock-watching and staring out of the window. But the hours are long, there is no annual leave, and I don't know when I can hand in my notice.

—

I look at my text conversations with her, laid out on my phone. A long daisy chain of words, saying *where are you?* and *sorry I had to rush off* and *I'm running behind as usual!* and *are you ok?* and *I hope things are feeling a bit less shit.* One of the designers of the first iPhone conceived this idea of putting all our conversations in a thread, with different-coloured speech bubbles to the right (me) and left (her). Every other phone manufacturer copied it and it became part of the invisible grammar shoring up our remote interactions.

The whole thread unspools like a two-hander, with both characters at first oblivious as to what's coming next and then all too aware but desperate to talk about anything else. Here she is, after the diagnosis, sending me a picture of an injured oystercatcher she has rescued, convalescing in a cardboard-box nest in her garden, its long orange beak peeking out sadly from the opening torn out of one side. Or excitedly sharing a picture of her old Brownie Collector's Badge, found in a clear-out. Then come the texts that say she is *feeling a bit rubbish, rallying a bit now. And sorry for going on and on, earlier. I could blame it on the drugs but you've known me too long.*

When you are ghosted, it feels like someone turned away from you in mid-conversation and walked silently out of the room

Then my words are parried with a bald *sorry, I can't talk right now* or *can I call you later?* When I got the first of those messages, my stomach dropped. She had never been so curt before; had someone stolen her phone? Then I twigged that it was an automated message, selected from a drop-down menu when she didn't have the energy to pick up. At the end comes a salvo of messages from me, with no reply. The ping-pong pattern on my phone fools me into thinking that a message will appear on the left, with her initial, but it never does.

When online daters cut off contact with someone they have been seeing by simply ignoring their messages, it is called 'ghosting'. What compounds the sense of abandonment, I assume, is that the speech-balloon format already implies a reply. When you are ghosted, it feels like someone turned away from you in mid-conversation and walked silently out of the room. Our age venerates interactivity. We think that every message deserves an answer, that no conversation need ever end. Back in the real world, though, plotlines peter out, conversations tail off and ends stay loose. Those deathless parting words we write and rewrite in our heads turn, in reality, into something bland and adamantly cheerful. The messages get briefer and more perfunctory and then, without warning, stop. But that's OK, or should be. Life is not a TV police procedural where, if the ending feels like a cop-out or doesn't tie up all the threads, you berate yourself for wasting twelve hours of your life. Our lives were precious anyway; they are not defined by the leaving of them.

—

Nowadays clinical psychologists don't tend to think like Freud. Grief, they have found, is not some exam we have to resit repeatedly until we learn to accept reality. Nor does it parse itself into neat, self-contained steps, from denial to bargaining to acceptance. Grief has no universal symptoms and no obligatory stages to be got through, like levels of a computer game. Most of us turn out to be fairly resilient in the face of loss. It doesn't tear us asunder. It just makes us feel wiped out and wobbly, and we wonder if this is really grief or if we are doing it wrong. Grief has no script; we are all just making it up as we go along.

Grief is not a long lesson in letting go. Maybe some of us never accept that the person we are grieving for no longer exists, and we learn to live with not accepting it. This is not magical thinking. We know that they are utterly gone, and for ever – but there they still are, brightly and intensely alive in our heads. In many cultures, the living see the dead as vividly present. On the Mexican Day of the Dead, they welcome their departed, always alive in memory and spirit, back to the earth. Maybe these rituals are on to something. Maybe grief, as a universal human dilemma, is something that evolution has hard-wired us to be able to handle, and this is one of the workarounds we have devised.

Something imagined is still real, because the imagination is real

Something imagined is still real, because the imagination is real. Most of what matters to us happens in our heads, in that supercomputer made of fat and protein between our ears. The unlived life is also life. I am forever conducting made-up conversations with others, endless rehearsals without a performance, or rehashing exchanges that went wrong, trying to do it better next time, even when I know there will never be a next time. That doesn't seem so different from the messages I compose to my friend in my head, which one day I might send zipping at the speed of light to that phone with the scuffed Cath Kidston case, which is probably still in a drawer somewhere, powered down but ready to sputter into life and pick up my unread messages. In our brains, synapses fire, chemicals react, electricity fizzes, new neural pathways form. What happens in our brains happens in the world, because our brains are part of the world.

—

At the end of August 2013, the poet Seamus Heaney was leaving a restaurant with a friend in Dublin, when he stumbled on the steps and banged his head. He was admitted to hospital, where the doctors found a split aorta, requiring a serious operation. After Heaney left for the operating room, he sent his wife Marie a text. It contained the Latin words *Noli timere*. Do not be afraid.

> **What happens in our brains happens in the world, because our brains are part of the world**

Heaney died shortly afterwards, before the operation even took place. His son Michael revealed these last words during his funeral eulogy, inspiring a flurry of tears in the congregation. Heaney had loved Latin ever since, as a small boy, he heard his mother rhyme off the Latin prefixes and suffixes she'd learned at school. He was old enough to have attended, in the days before Vatican II, daily Latin masses at St Columb's, the Catholic grammar school he went to on a scholarship. He learned Latin in its classrooms, where it was taught in imitation of the English public schools, and his lifelong love of Virgil began. He admired the relentless logic of the language, its economy and precision, its neat conflation of analytical and emotional truth. *Noli timere* says with two words what English needs four to say, or, in the King James Bible, three: *Be not afraid.* Two words are easier to type when you're being wheeled to theatre on a trolley.

Noli timere appears about seventy times in St Jerome's Vulgate Bible. Often God says it, while trying to calm a human understandably freaked out at His presence. The angel says it to the shepherds before bringing them news of the birth of Jesus. Jesus says it to the disciples when he walks on water, and when he meets them after rising from the dead. The force of *Noli timere* derives from its blend of clear instruction and gentle assurance.

Heaney's texted words weren't as lapidary or final as all that. He was expected to recover from the operation, and often used Latin with his family as a private, joking language. His use of the singular form *noli timere* instead of the plural *nolite timere* suggests the message was personal, meant only for his wife. But the family, Michael later wrote, 'seized on his final words as a kind of lifebuoy'. It seemed to them that he had captured 'the swirl of emotion, uncertainty and fear he was facing at the end, and articulated it in a restrained yet inspiring way'. *Noli timere* was a last act of kindness, a spell to help those left behind to grieve.

In the days and weeks after Heaney's death, *Noli timere* appeared in all the obituaries and tributes. They became a shorthand for the power of language to help us survive our losses. They did what Heaney had been doing for more than half a century: writing sturdy, well-shaped words that cut cleanly through banality and pierced the heart. The graffiti artist Maser painted the words, in English, on a gable end wall in Portobello, Dublin (although an all-caps DON'T BE AFRAID in massive white letters is not perhaps as reassuring as it is trying to be). The phrase now speaks a little more forlornly in our fretful and fractious new world, from which Heaney was spared.

A few months after my friend died, this story about Heaney's last words came into my head. It felt like a little chink of light to walk towards, a source of solace and hope. It made me see that a virtual goodbye could still be beautiful, that a message sent through the ether might mean even more for being so intangible and precarious. The written word can be an outstretched hand across the abyss; it can walk through walls.

—

The most common way of thinking about our online lives, even among people who spend most of their lives online, is that they are unreal. To be online is to be disembodied, reduced to eyes and fingertips, occupying some elusive other realm, made of air and vapour. The web is eating up our lives, we fear, and disgorging them as a waking dream, or fooling us into thinking that some better life is being lived elsewhere, just out of reach. We have gone down a rabbit hole of our own making. If it weren't all so addictive, we would come to our senses, power down our devices and return to the three-dimensional sensorium of real life.

But that's not right, is it? I mean, we should probably spend less time doomscrolling and hate-reading and getting pointlessly angry with strangers. And maybe we shouldn't lie in the dark so much after midnight, kept awake by the flickering light of our phones and the adrenaline rush that comes from eavesdropping on the babble of other people's egos begging to be affirmed. But still, our online lives are also our lives – extensions of our humanity, not some pitiable stand-in for it. *Man is an animal,* the anthropologist Clifford Geertz once wrote, *suspended in webs of significance he himself has spun.*

> **But still, our online lives are also our lives – extensions of our humanity, not some pitiable stand-in for it**

Like us, the online world is both physical and ethereal. It is made of wireless routers, modems with blinking lights, vast data centres in unmarked buildings full of humming hard drives and glass fibres inside copper tubes, and hundreds of thousands of miles of cable, buried alongside roads and railways and crossing ocean floors, occasionally nibbled at by sharks. And it is also made of our lusts and rages and fears and desires, which are more real to us than our livers and kidneys.

And what do we learn in this virtual world that is nowhere near as virtual as we think? Only that the deepest connections between us are the most fragile, because they are made of that filigree web of meaning and mutual care we all spin together. And we also learn that absence needn't mean obliteration, that someone you can't see or hear can still exist – that objects, even human objects, have permanence.

—

I wonder how all those people who had to say their final goodbyes on FaceTime are doing now. I imagine they were as angry as I was when the gaslighting sociopaths of Downing Street told them to *draw a line and move on*. I assume they felt the same guilt that I did about obeying the rules when the rule makers didn't. We feel guilty, as the historian Elaine Pagels says, because it is more bearable than feeling helpless, than falling through an unending chasm of meaninglessness. It follows that guilt is assuaged when we find meaning again. So I hope those people have come round to the idea that their online partings were still meaningful, and that they did, after all, convey something profound about human love – that the ties that bind us are as tenuous and transient as life itself, and yet they are made of the strongest material in the universe.

After all those texts I sent with no reply, I did get a final message. She must have found, on her phone, one of those firms that send flowers in a slim cardboard package that fits through your letterbox. On the day she died, a dozen stems of solidago and alstroemeria arrived, with a card. *All love to you my most amazing friend*, it said. *It seems unfair that men don't get given things that smell nice.* I wonder if, like me, she was thankful in the end for our soullessly algorithmic online world – the one that requires us only to swipe and prod a glass screen to magic up flower pickers and delivery drivers and have our words, tapped out with our thumbs, transcribed in cards with handwritten fonts. I finally threw the flowers out after a month, when all but a few of the petals had shrivelled and shed. But I still have the card – my own *Noli timere*. **⊞**

In Billions of Years the Sun Will Swallow the Earth

by Jarred McGinnis

2016

To be able to take a full year of maternity leave, we left London to live cheaply elsewhere and happily reduced the world to our immediate and newly expanded family of three. On that first day in Mexico, baby Poe was tucked against my wife's chest in a wrap, completely incurious about the setting sun drawing closer to the grey-blue endlessness of the Pacific. On the dark rocks nearby, brown pelicans struck poses regal and absurd. Around us was the marvel of purple shadows flanking the horizon that could have been mountains or clouds.

I was enjoying the familiar humidity and heat from my childhood spent in the subtropics of Southwest Florida after these past adult decades beneath the low-hung grey chill of London. Shirtless men armed with cast nets battled over a plunder of fish with frigatebirds, an animal made for war with its long-bladed wings. What do you call these fish? I asked a whip of a boy, wearing only Spider-Man underwear. He threw the dagger-shaped fish into a bucket. 'Cariños', he said. I looked up the word. It means sweetheart.

We arrived in May, the off-season. The Old Town of Puerto Vallarta is a grid of colonial buildings full of gay bars to entertain older and wealthier American tourists who come for the mild winters here. The tourism board has been trying to rebrand the area as Zona Romantica. There's a bar called 'Wet Dreams' with a sign that says 'No Women'. Inside, you can order a beer and watch a handsome young man suds his body in a glass shower, which is romance of a kind. People live in the Zona as well. The shaded stairwells between buildings are full of families poking at their phones as they hide from the day's heat. Old Town is separated from the America-in-miniature walled resorts to the north by the trickle of the Rio Cuale. Further north and closer to the airport, the pretence of Mexico is dropped completely and it is just strip malls of McDonalds and TGI Fridays.

The Spanish of Mexico is best for baby talk. Chubby-ankled syllables and round, rolling Rs make it a perfect language to give your newborn more nicknames than an ancient god: Cariño, abejita, bonita, chamaquita, preciosa, tierna. Everyone there was baby crazy. Gangs of tattooed teenage boys cooed as much as the frequent encirclements of grandmas. We had to get used to strangers rubbing our baby's head and brushing her cheek uninvited. Our walks along the promenade were interrupted every few feet to let anyone from the police to fishermen make silly faces and invoke one of her thousand nicknames. I loved it. A whole nation sharing the marvel of this small human's existence. One of my favourite theonyms for her was chuleta (pork chop). It invoked her pudge of thigh and dimpled knee.

They thought my daughter was a boy. She was an exceptionally bald baby. Head perfectly round. Big eyes, still newborn indigo. She resembled a 1:12 scale model of a Soviet politburo member. We were told over and over that baby girls have their ears pierced at the hospital. I had compounded the problem by thinking it was funny to dress her in baby-sized guayabera shirts that matched my own. To make matters worse, we gave her an unusual name, Poe Zula Rose. The owner of a taqueria misunderstood us and thought her name was Popote (drinking straw), which immediately became Popotito (skinny minnie). Of all the nicknames that we brought back with us from Mexico, we still use this one. My sweetheart, my pork chop, my Popotito.

She was an exceptionally bald baby. Head perfectly round ... She resembled a 1:12 scale model of a Soviet politburo member

One day, we burned the baby. We were looking for a post office and got turned around in the grid of sidewalks three feet above the streets clotted with CENTRO buses and yellow cabs that catcall 'taxi' at us. The cost of our mistake was stripes of sunburn on our daughter's arms and legs where she poked out from her mother's wrap. We stopped so Poe could take a nap under a beach palapa to hide from the sun and make the most of a welcome ocean breeze. The grey foil shimmer of a calm sea was before us and an oversaturated sky above. Poe was naked except for her diaper and a wet cloth on her head to cool her down. Though she was more fussy than usual, she didn't, couldn't, blame me. I asked for forgiveness anyway, dabbing at her sunburn with aloe harvested from the landscaping of a hotel.

I settled her down on my bare chest. She was still baby-tiny but, at almost double her birth weight, substantial in a new way. Of all the clichés about parenting, no one talks about how easy time travel becomes. That moment with our skin touching and the compact weight of her, balled up as if still in utero, whipped us forward nine months. Poe is one. We are back in London and in our own flat. Maternity leave has ended and Sarah is back at work. Poe is still stubbornly bald but she is crawling and starting to walk by holding on to my wheelchair and working her way around me, giggling with excitement at her new ability. She drops back down to crawl away and aims straight for a plug, which she puts in her mouth. I yell at her, a forceful 'no' from fear more than anger. I scoop her up and feel the heart racing within the fragile shell of ribs as she draws breath to work herself into an ugly pantomime cry. I spent my first forty years questioning whether I could be a good man, using definitions handed down but always ill-fitting. Forty years to feel confident that I had made another life different from never feel, never cry, never apologize. I had become a man without that exhausting need for obedience and violence that had been my inheritance. But, this little girl will be scared of me. I will be frightening just as my father was frightening to me and his father to him.

'Are you OK?' Sarah said to me. Poe was a diapered three-month-old again, asleep and tucked against me, my hand rubbing her back. I was back on the beach in Mexico. Sarah had returned with a bottle of 'child-safe' sun cream. I said I was fine but in me was the knowledge that I would be the one to seed fear into my daughter's heart.

2020
As the virus's exponential growth stopped everything else, it was easy to fold away the life we had returned to in London. Our daughter is four now. The reserves of fat on her thighs have been used up to stretch out her limbs. The baby that everyone thought was a boy is clearly a little girl now. I still struggle to order the many persons my daughter is and has been: the newborn with her rattling cry, the six-month-old with her constant look of bewilderment and easy-come smiles, the fists full of 'no!s' toddler and now the little girl who I confidently tell the babysitter, 'if there's anything I've missed, ask the four-year-old.' I am eager to linger among her past selves, to revisit, to understand the permutations of her so that I can make the best use of the brief time I have with the next Poe I am to meet. She, on the other hand, goads the pace of the leaps forward. I am a fixed point. A promontory by which she calculates her speed of travel.

After our year travelling with newborn Poe, we knew how to live small. Furloughed, we became tourists in our own city. In our hour of exercise, we discovered a handful of churchyards and tucked-away green spaces that we had ignored in the decade of living in Bethnal Green, East London. The portents of 2016 have unfolded and our anxieties now are more general, unspecific but pervasive. I no longer wonder if I am a good man, because there are no good men, nor bad either. I am to my family an accumulation of moments. I think the balance, so far, favours me.

As the virus's exponential growth stopped everything else, it was easy to fold away the life we had returned to in London

This pause in our lives has exacerbated the leaps in time. They are never consistent or stable and I suppose this adds to the discomfort. It's the leaps forward that are still the most painful. It happened the other day. Poe was playing on a tree stump in St Matthew's churchyard near our flat. This has been a favourite spot of ours during lockdown. There was rarely anyone there and the occasional dog walker, jogger or addict always kept their distance. The eighteenth-century stone walls let Poe range without me worrying about traffic or kidnappings. The patterned trunks of the ancient and giant London plane trees like castle towers guard the perimeter of the yard, providing shade and sticks for us to build fairy forts. I am a fan of the mild English summer and its autumn turning. I endure the dark winter, because it makes spring more of an event. Growing up near the Tropic of Cancer, the difference in the length of day throughout the year is barely noticeable. Time was harder to measure there.

Poe and I are watching a snail make its way across the lip of a stump. The undulations of its wet green leathery foot and tentacles are beautiful. Poe turns her body toward me, hands on my wheelchair, but her eyes are transfixed. She whimpers and buries her face against my lap, but her gaze returns to the slow tap of its lower tentacles. I say, don't be afraid, and demonstrate by touching its eye stalk. It pauses and the black spot of its eye pulls back into its body then extends again. This draws her attention. She puts her own small hand out, finger extended, but turns away. Then, she does it. She pokes a snail in the eye. She is excited and proud. She chitters about how she is a big girl, she is brave. It will be the first thing she tells her mom that night.

The shifts in time come with no warning, no sense of foreboding, no tingling spines. It just happens

She is meant to start reception in September, but Covid has made that uncertain. Primary school years have been a recurring topic for Poe. As the snail makes its deliberate but ponderous escape from our poking, she asks what Year you are in when you are eight. The twang of cockney in her accent makes me smile. Having not grown up in England, I have to do a little extra transcription to convert American elementary grades to British primary years. You'll be in Year three or four, I tell her. She picks up a stick to thwack the stump and says that she is eleven. I inform her that at that age she is in secondary school. She is impressed by this information. I ask her what it is like being eleven. For her, eleven means she can walk to school on her own and climb trees. You climb trees now, I suggest. She explains that eleven-year-olds climb trees really high. OK, I say.

She wanders off pretending to be an eleven-year-old. With her stick, she measures the depth of an old fox hole in the southeast corner of the churchyard. London is quiet without its cars and people. Quiet except for the air ambulances that rush toward the Royal London. Sometimes there is a queue of red helicopters making circles over our flat. A man in his home office looks down at us, watching Poe and smiling.

The shifts in time come with no warning, no sense of foreboding, no tingling spines. It just happens. Poe turns her head and runs back toward me in that funny stiff-arm way children run. It is as if a transparency has been brought down over the scene. I see her as a four-year-old overlaid with the young woman she will be. I recall memories of her teenage years that I have yet to experience. Twenty years are crossed and there is anxiety over an issue she was having, will have, might have. She has a decision to make. The kind of decision that only a young woman has to make and she has turned to me, her father, for advice. Her eyes are wet and her neck has gone blotchy red from worry. She sits on a sea wall on a beach in a place that I have yet to live. I smell the sea and the pepper of pines from my Floridian childhood. The familiar whiff of marine diesel is there too and I wonder what circumstances would have precipitated me ever moving back to Florida. But I don't recognize this beach. The sea is clear and still like the Gulf of Mexico but the water more topaz than the turquoise I remember. Beyond my adult daughter is a bright clear day and a hill mottled with dark pines and buildings of dusty pink. There are no hills in Florida.

Poe is talking and I strain to hear her from twenty years in the past. I'm keen to suggest options without prescribing solutions, aware that I only know a fraction of this young woman's life. A couple walking past us are speaking French, trying not to look at Poe, who is clearly upset, and the old man beside her. Have we moved to France? Poe has shed my definitions of her but our relationship feels intact there in the future and it fills me with relief. A thought comes to me: we are in Marseille. There is the striped shadow of the Calanques bowing toward the Mediterranean. The large tower blocks are pitiable beneath that banded architecture eons in its construction. Then it is over.

My four-year-old, and only her, reaches me. She puts her arms and head in my lap. I pet her hair; it is the same colour as Sarah's with a bit of my curl to it. In her child's face, the eyes, brows, chin and lips of the woman she will be are already there. This Future Poe is rushing to meet me and it scares me. I'm not ready. Present Poe is calling to her to hurry, and it feels a betrayal no matter how inevitable. Poe asks me a question but I'm too overwhelmed by the experience. I suggest a snack and she asks if I have dried mango.

As we walk back to the flat, I am still thinking about the strange experience while she negotiates for screen time to watch a movie. She has been very good all day, she argues. Maybe by moving to France, we could stuff full our Now with the newness, confusion, excitement, stress of living in a foreign country again. Maybe with my head occupied with formulating sentences like, 'Où est l'aire de jeux?' Poe will be less likely to slip away into the future. Maybe twenty years becomes an indetectable span of time while I watch the sea, the oldest of Earth's gods, rumble and hiss while she plays in its foam.

I pet her hair: it is the same colour as Sarah's with a bit of my curl to it. In her child's face, the eyes, brows, chin and lips of the woman she will be are already there

We pass a row of terraced houses. The first has rose bushes. I gently bend the stems so that she can sniff the blooms. She recommends the orange ones as the best. I agree. The second house has a single and enormous lavender full of a variety of bees. We listen to the hum and watch the flower spikes nod and bounce as the fat, fuzzy ones land and alight. This is the queen of lavenders, I am informed by Poe. At the third and final house, a common poppy has exploded from a crack where the pavement meets a wall of yellow London stock brick. The poppy's green stalks rise arrow straight. She pulls

off the red paper petals. I wish she wouldn't.
Poppy blooms are already too brief, but I say 'no'
too much as it is so I let her. Yesterday, we had
wandered the town armed with chalk. Her graffiti
of POPPY remains above the plant. She plucks off

**I tell lots of stories to Poe. You could ungenerously
but accurately call them lies. I have told her
that Queen Elizabeth is a twenty-foot giant**

a pod and dissects it to examine the seeds. Without
looking up at me she asks to hear the stories about
when she was a tiny baby. I tell lots of stories to
Poe. You could ungenerously but accurately call
them lies. I have told her that Queen Elizabeth is
a twenty-foot giant, which is why she needs such
a large house like Buckingham Palace. For now,
I prefer Poe living in a world where a giant has a
house that is appropriate for her size rather than
the normal-sized woman benefiting from her uncle's
taste for American rough. She has heard the story
of when she was a tiny baby countless times. She
has asked for the story countless more. It pleases me
that it pleases her and, after my experience in the
churchyard, I'm eager to return to assurances of the
past. I tell her once again. When she was born, she
was tiny tiny tiny and we took her to a faraway land
called Mexico. She rode in my shirt pocket during
the day and waved at all the people smiling at the
incredibly tiny, bald baby. At night, she slept beside
us on the beach in her own coquina shell. A fluff of
coconut fibre for a pillow, a corner of a tortilla for a
blanket. For fun, she rode on the back of a minnow

in the Rio Cuale. That is why we call her 'Popotito'.
She smiles and nods at her recognition of the story.
   After scattering the commas of poppy seed like
I showed her yesterday to sow more flowers among
the cracks, she leads us home. The charcoal smudge
of the Calanques cuts the horizon above our flat.
We have the ground floor, and the wall around our
patio garden is hidden by the jasmine vines that we
planted when we moved in a decade ago. It's the
longest we have ever lived in one place. These cliffs
do not look down on East London of our now. They
stand above Poe and I somewhere and some day
in the future. I was raised in the brutal flatness of
Florida. Every year hurricanes came to scrub the
peninsula clean of human error. As a child I made
blood sacrifices to the ancient cypress swamps,
my offering carried by grey clouds of mosquitoes.
If I was to believe in God, it would be of the Old
Testament, all caprice and smite. In this France
I've seen, we had a benign permanence high-above
watching over my family. The idea appeals to me.
I could go to this landscape, now quickly fading
above the glass and steel palisade of Canary Wharf.
Give my daughter hills and mountains to add to her
drawings of our family. Give her a beach to play on,
let her know the marvels I knew growing up by the
sea, but without its dangers: wet sand between toes,
the taste of salt waves and flocks of seagulls like
ticker tape above our picnics.
   There in our future Poe will meet an old man
she knows as her dad. She will have to reconcile
him with the omnipotent, omniscient father that

child Poe has confused me for. She will look back at the past and see that the magic I used to open the parking gate was a remote in my pocket. That manhole covers are just manhole covers and not from where street-cleaning monkeys emerge at night to sweep up the goober-eggs; my name for used nitrous canisters. There is no avoiding that as a parent, I will disappoint her, but that glimpse of twenty years hence gives me the hope that I will never fail her. And, I hope not to confuse that woman she becomes with the little girl scared of snails or the little baby sunburned by my inattention. It will be hard; they are all here with me at every moment. ◨

A compelling portrait of the prominent artist who shaped the development of performance art in Asia.

"Chan Li Shan offers readers a biography of a fascinating and important performance artist; a memoir of her own experience as his biographer, collaborator, and friend; and an innovative, nuanced, often moving mosaic of interview excerpts, testimonials from friends and admirers, timelines linking Singapore's history to Lee Wen's own, striking photographs, and meditations on the act of representing a life."

—Craig Howes, Director, Center for Biographical Research, Professor of English, University of Hawai'i at Mānoa

Get your copy at epigrambookshop.sg.

EPIGRAM BOOKS

The Right Thing

by Munizha Ahmad-Cooke

he train leaves us exposed on the platform at Whittlesford station and snatches away the lull of being in transit. All that is left now is the walkway that crosses over the tracks. I straighten, tightening my grip around the straps of my overnight shoulder bag.

'He might not be here, darling. Had a feeling when I spoke to him on the phone. But that's OK, we can get a cab. Like we did that other time.'

She shrugs and shoves her phone into the back pocket of her jeans, 'Should have done that anyway.'

'Well, I wasn't sure. I could be wrong.'

Dread mounts with each concrete stair we climb, and I want to run back to the train and rewind to the soporific huddle of my elderly parents' house. As we reach the steps at the other end of the narrow bridge, we spot the car. Perhaps I am wrong. Perhaps it will be good to be home. Perhaps he finally got those shelves up.

'Good weekend? How is everyone?' he cuts in before I can get to the end of the word 'Hi' and into the passenger seat. Old dismay, so easily awoken, stirs in the pit of my stomach.

'Yeah, good,' I smile, trying to match his breezy tone. 'You OK?' I scan his profile as he fixes his look ahead, his eyes unavailable to mine.

'Hmm? Yeeaahhh,' he affects in that 'same-as-ever' drawl, flicking a glance my way. Old dismay is stretching out inside me now, its stale breath climbing my throat and souring the taste in my mouth.

The three of us focus on what's outside our windows. The September evening light is dwindling. It's barely a ten-minute drive, but I am just too weary to endure it.

'Stop the car.'

'Huh?'

'Stop the car. I'll drive.'

There is no protest, no affronted look. Now, in this recovery–relapse cycle, he at least spares me his indignance, no longer forcing me to spell out my accusation while he repeatedly denies it, fixing me with reddened eyes or exhaling his extra-strong-mint breath in my face as proof. It could be that we have made some progress. It could be that we're just tired.

We circle the car – me around the back, him round the front. I force myself not to look at him and assess the steadiness of his walk, either to confirm I am right or to double-check in case I am wrong. I am trying to practise what I preach to our daughter, whose big brown eyes – wide open from the moment she was born – I can feel watching us from the back seat, anticipating the drama: 'Trust your gut. Most times it will be right, and it doesn't matter if you're sometimes wrong. It's the lies and self-doubt and the guilt you feel for being suspicious that drive you crazy.'

As we continue the journey, the silence returns, but rather than pressing down on us, it is building towards a release. I pull into our drive.

'It's over for me, I'm afraid.' I am calm and still and tearless. The house waits in the glow of the security light that has just come on. The home of our own we finally staggered into three years ago after a decade of lugging more and more stuff from one rented place to another. Even I am shocked by my words, but I guess when you've reached the end they just speak themselves.

**'It's over for me, I'm afraid' ...
Even I am shocked by my words, but I guess when you've reached the end they just speak themselves**

Inside, we scatter into separate rooms. I flop onto the takhat in our living room. The hushed thud of the cupboard and the tin-glass twist of the lid of the whiskey bottle in the kitchen behind me, sounds that once alerted every nerve, only add to my numbness. As he mumbles his way up the stairs, I cannot even steal a sideways glance to see if he is taking the bottle up with him, no doubt clasped to his far side like the secret it somehow still needs to be. The small of my back presses against the unmatching bolsters that travelled with the takhat from my parents' house. The larger of the two is covered in the once-lush John Lewis curtain fabric my newlywed sister bought for her first home 30 years ago. Salvaged from the wreckage of that marriage by my mother, its Klimtian circles within circles of gold, emerald and magenta have faded and, in some places, worn to a small hole or tear. At one end the white kamarband that draws it together like the waistband of a salwar has come undone and disappeared inside its neatly stitched casing. I remind myself again to sort it out while I summon the stamina to piece back together the rest of this evening.

From halfway down the stairs, my daughter looks in through the doorway, phone in hand.

'Mum? Mum! Do you really mean it this time?'

'What?'

'When you said you and Dad were finished?'

I nod once, as though for the first time, staring ahead at the darkening slits of parked cars and still Sunday-night homes through the blind.

'So, you're really going to do it?'

I am dazed by her urgent glare. 'Yes.'

'Hi, Mia? Yeah, she said yes, *definitely*. They're going to get divorced.' She races back upstairs carrying on her conversation. The news is out. Year 8 have it on record.

I am up. The half-cooked roast chicken he took out of the oven when we got home lies abandoned on the worktop. The skin he normally takes such pride in crisping to perfection is clammy and pale. I walk up the stairs, preparing myself for the familiar sight of him passed out on the bed. As I see him, washed up and bloated by the ocean of cheap whiskey he has drowned himself in for over a decade, I exhale, extinguishing the flicker of hope I was still nursing of saving our marriage, or at least the evening, or at the very least dinner.

'Facing up to things as usual?' I can't keep the contempt out of my voice. His mother has started pushing the button on the doorbell she uses to call us from her annexe: *ping-ping, As-Salaam-Alaikum!* it squalls. On good days, the ring tone we have selected from a revolving repertoire adds a smile to the summons, a glint of mischief to our life as dutiful carers. He half opens his eyes and I feel myself blur. Turning over and closing them again, he slurs 'I'll do anything, give me to the end of the year.'

Ping-ping, As-Salaam-Alaikum!
I take my time, measuring each step, slowing down each breath. I walk into her annexe, stretching my face into a smile as I approach her beige velvet riser-recliner chair from behind. The ceiling of the converted garage feels lower than usual as I meet her small, agitated eyes.
'What's happening? Is he alright?'
'He's drunk.'
'Oh?' She wrinkles her forehead, 'Where is he?'
'Asleep in bed. I'll go and sort out some dinner.' I conjure a reassuring look as I leave, knowing that it won't be long before she's pushing that fucking button again.
Ping-ping, As-Salaam-Alaikum!
'Is he OK?'
'He's just had too much to drink. He's asleep.'
Pasta, I resolve.
Ping-ping, As-Salaam-Alaikum!
'He's never been drunk before,' she informs me with a baffled and baffling certainty. I feel the urge to both scream at her and hold her hand at the same time.

'He's an alcoholic. You just don't remember.'
You even sympathised with me once, quite
affectionately, when things were bad in the old
house, I want to say, but I don't have the energy to
go down that rabbit hole.
　　Ping-ping, As-Salaam-Alaikum!
　　I had drifted off. The pan of boiling water in
front of me is at fury point.

| **You even sympathised with me once,
quite affectionately ... I want to say, but I don't
have the energy to go down that rabbit hole**

'If he gets up, don't go on and on at him,' she
entreats, as though defending a naughty toddler to
an angry parent. I look at her. I am tipping towards
the scream. Just get dinner done, I tell myself. The
carer will be here soon; I can say goodnight and
shut the annexe door. I can say goodnight and shut
my daughter's door, then our bedroom door, and
then the door of the spare room where I can lie still
and silent and alone in the dark.

When I get to the fold-out mattress, and under
my duvet with the white cotton cover from my
single days that always soothes my sight, my mum's
Urdu words join the swirl in my head: 'A woman
makes a home, and a woman breaks it.' I had felt
at once empowered and frustrated at those words
when she had pronounced them like a universal
truth. I wanted to argue, but the word aurat stood
tall in my mind. I was that woman, the possessor
of a golden thread that held everything together.

How gracefully I held on to it and managed
its tension through every tremor. But I had not
noticed it stealthily wrapping itself around me like
a vine, smothering my heart, crushing my voice.
I spread myself out beneath the duvet, tracing
the embroidered flower shapes on the cover over
my chest and belly. On the pillow beside me is
Deborah Levy's *The Cost of Living*, the searing
words of a newly divorced middle-aged woman
who is 'dissolving and recomposing', having chosen
to swim into the tempest rather than back to the
'leaking boat' of her marriage and its 'symbolic
protection'. Words I will cling to as I enter my own
storm. The unyielding yellow of the book's sleeve
radiates across my vast white plain where I let go of all
threads and allow the stories in my custody to unravel.

This was not the worst incident by far, but by then
the threshold had been worn to the ground. For a
year or so, we had been the success story. We had
countered the odds. I left each of the Inclusion
workshops for friends and families of addicts, which
I attended only as insurance, with a sense of relief
that we had made it out of the darkness so many of
the other attendees were trapped in. People told me
how strong I had been, which puzzled me at first.
To have put up with it in silence for so long, to have
been his unwitting enabler did not feel strong. Most
of the time I had simply not known what to do, just
like everyone in that room of despairing parents,
partners and children of addicts, gratefully soaking
up information about addictive behaviour, co-

dependency and the clashing ego states we and our addicts communicate from. Everyone doing their best to understand and gather hope while their eyes screamed 'Please, just tell me what to do!'

I had tried every approach I could think of: compassion, anger, encouraging him to get help, tiptoeing around triggering conversations, threatening to leave, reasoning and pleading, or 'ignoring' it, as my mother advised, and pursuing my own interests. But it envelops you as much as it envelops them. As he sank deeper into the bottle, I circled its thin, slippery rim like a tightrope walker, keeping up my watchful performance, forced to be the responsible, unerring, vigilant one. I felt cheated of the adventure I had sought in this rebellious, creative, witty, intelligent man.

In the end, there is only one timeless, repetitive truth: an addict can only stop if they really want to. Nonetheless, the curse of the one who loves them most is to keep trying to push that bloody rock up that bloody hill, telling themselves each time it rolls back to the bottom, whether lower or higher than last time, that now things might change. More than two years after our separation, I am still only beginning to realise and accept three simple facts:

One: for most of our marriage, bar the euphoric year of recovery, he had no desire to stop – something I could not, or refused, to see. Two: wherever you place it on the spectrum from illness to wilfulness, there is no logic to addiction; lapses and relapses are always on the horizon and need no reason, although you can always find one. And thus, three: however much you try to understand it as a non-addict, you never will. It resists and defies common sense and order, like romantic love, like the randomness of life.

I defied common sense when I married someone I knew to have issues with addiction. It made our marriage so much more poetic and intoxicating. And knowing that I had gone in with my eyes wide open took away, I felt, my entitlement to say I didn't want to live with it anymore, as well as my entitlement to sympathy. Now, while I understand a little more each day that my decision that September Sunday evening was the right thing for us all, that it is OK to put yourself first and that healthy boundaries and expectations are a must, there will always be a part of me that feels she failed at love.

When the afternoon sun slants in through the blinds, she is 26 once more and full of bliss. It is Monday. She packs up the books she has not been reading and slips out of the library, again abandoning the PhD research she has fallen into because she has always been a good student and a little afraid of life. She alights at Barbican Tube station, her steps buoyed by summer and desire. Her sand-coloured cotton shift dress – a perfect just-tight-enough fit – checked with colourful threads, the warmth of the pavement beneath her sandalled feet and her sun-tinted skin create a glow around her she is sure everyone can see. She grins to herself as she enters a newsagent and selects a tub of strawberries and cream Haagen-Dazs.

When he opens the door of his converted warehouse, she holds out her offering, playfully winking at the glint in his eye. They giggle at the tingle of the shower on their skin, the ecstasy they took at the party two nights before still drifting through her and coursing through him with all he has added to it since. Water drips from her hair and body as she leads the way to his mezzanine bed. As he climbs the ladder to join her, she watches him take in each shimmering detail of her nakedness as though he has reached an oasis in the desert. They explore, discover and devour each other, tearing down boundaries, sweat and ice-cream pinkness soaking into the sheet.

I defied common sense when I married someone I knew to have issues with addiction. It made our marriage so much more poetic and intoxicating

When she wakes, the Clerkenwell room is immersed in a Mediterranean afternoon light. Her dress a whisper on the floor amid the stacks of vinyl propped along the full length of the walls. She reaches for a book from the shelf beside the bed. *Words* by Jean-Paul Sartre. Affirmation that she and him, like Sartre and de Beauvoir, are the freest of spirits, the most exquisite of soulmates, blazing their path. Her dreamy focus alternates between the page, his dark brow, the slim red line of his lips and the angles of his svelte body beneath the cotton sheet. This day has carved out a home inside her and, now and then, it will light up and bring her back, planting soft kisses on her wet cheeks and caressing away any traces of regret. **H**

WE CIRCLE SILENTLY ABOUT THE WRECK

by Elizabeth Norton

1.   The ocean wants me. I believe this recklessly,
     without footnotes. At night, on the innards of
     my eyelids, behold the ecstatic glare of sunlight
     bouncing off the surface of the water. And
     I feel that water nuzzling my ankles, even
     in the grey city, even when I sleep, the low
     yellow burn of street lights spilling across my
     bedroom floor.

2.   Throughout my childhood, I believe this want
     is virtuous. So I let the ocean pull me in, I let
     the water prune my fingers and toes. Blood
     vessels shrinking from the shock of the cold. I
     trust it to take me in, to let me go again. And
     then, so incrementally that I do not realise I
     am changing, I lose my trust. It is not what
     the water takes from me. It is what the world
     takes, as I move through it, it is what my body
     learns about the edge. I step back, but the
     waves come for me anyway.

3.   I learn to swim before I can remember not
     being able to swim. Lessons with my older
     brother and a teacher who is mean to us
     equally. At the local leisure centre, in the
     baby pool first, moving up to the main pool.
     I swim twice a week, three times a week.
     There is something about being submerged
     in an indoor pool, bright lights, looking out
     on a winter's night. An echoing gladness
     to be within rather than without. There is
     something about the smell of chlorine. It still

makes my fingers tingle, the hair on the back of my neck prickle.

4. As a child, I entertain an obsession with the freediver, Tanya Streeter. She dives in a silver all-in-one suit, stretching the length of her limbs and around her head, only her face exposed. I like it most when she wears a monofin that webs her legs and feet together like a mermaid. No tank on her back, she dives on a single breath held for over six minutes. After one of her documentaries airs on the BBC, I compose an email to her on the family computer. I tell her I would like to be a freediver just like her.

5. When we breathe in, our diaphragm and intercostal muscles contract, creating a vacuum in our chest cavity. Oxygen-rich air floods our windpipe, which splits into our right and left bronchus, becomes our many-branched bronchioles. Clusters of alveoli, like berries at the end of tree branches, absorb the air. Here, inside these fuchsia berries, the life-sustaining exchange of oxygen and carbon dioxide across a permeable membrane. Oxygen-rich blood is pumped to the cells of the body. Normally, we exhale the waste air out and the process begins again.

6. Streeter holds the women's world record for so-called no-limits freediving. In August 2002

she dives to a depth of 525 feet. That is deeper than Blackpool Tower is tall; approximately the length of five football pitches. In no-limits freediving, divers descend on a metal sled on a rope which takes them deeper and deeper into the blue, navy, black. When they reach their desired depth, they pull a pin on a bag of compressed air that inflates and propels them back to the surface. All this on a single breath held for several minutes.

7. When we hold our breath, the oxygen saturation of our blood falls, and the carbon dioxide builds. The increase in carbon dioxide triggers the urge to breathe out. We fight that urge and it continues to grow. Our chest burns and our diaphragm begins to convulse. At the breath-hold breakpoint, we cannot hold it anymore. The carbon dioxide is intolerable to our brain and it is no longer our choice. We involuntarily breathe out.

8. Streeter describes freediving as travelling to the edge of herself. On her world-record-breaking dive, she messes up. Ordinarily, nitrogen in our lungs does not absorb into the bloodstream. But the deeper one goes with a held breath, the more nitrogen finds its way into the blood and the brain. It induces narcosis. A state of euphoria or intoxication; hallucinations, confusion. When the metal sled reaches the bottom of the rope, instead

of pulling the pin on her compressed oxygen, Streeter blows a kiss to the ocean. She wastes valuable seconds, unmoving, not cognisant of her mistake. I watch grainy footage of this dive online. Despite knowing how it ends, my heart begins to crawl up my throat.

9. When we involuntarily breathe out in water, we panic, and then we inhale, inviting water into our airways. This is called aspiration. If we aspirate well enough, if water penetrates the airways far enough, it reaches our alveoli. The life-sustaining exchange of oxygen and carbon dioxide stops. We are internally flooded.

10. At secondary school, we swim as a class once a week. In the diving pit, the deepest pool, I take a breath and dive down. I retrieve an orange, plastic body from the bottom and carry it to the surface. I like to do this. I like to be seen to do this. The power of my lungs, my legs.

11. The women in the changing room. Women made of lines and bellies and protruding bones, of cells and fibres and aortic valves. They stand with their feet planted apart, sinewy legs like tree roots. They laugh from the deepest parts of their throats with heads tilted back, wet hair dripping down sun-mottled skin. They laugh with their nipples out and pubic hair glistening. I try to imagine

myself grown like that but it is as absurd as trying to imagine myself never born. Women, skin hot from the shower, tinged red. I blink and they are carcasses, slow-cooking in the steam. Now, I am grown like that. And I know we carry it always, naked or clothed, outdoors or at home. We carry that bloated death-potential. That abattoir gleam.

12. In the poem 'Diving into the Wreck', Adrienne Rich writes about a woman who dives, alone, to explore a shipwreck. The diver has read the book of myths about the wreck and now she has come to see *the thing itself and not the myth*. It is widely known that Rich was a feminist, that she was writing about the oppression and erasure of women throughout history, the need to interrogate established facts, to go below the surface and confront the wreckage. She acknowledges the solitude of the woman who undertakes this expedition, carrying *a knife, a camera/a book of myths/in which/our names do not appear.* We love poems that bond us, that we can share.

13. Some poems change us. These poems are not collective, they are ours alone. Rich is telling me to put on my *body-armor of black rubber/the absurd flippers/the grave and awkward mask*. She is warning me of the absurdity of this life, how to suit up, how silly it will seem until I feel like I want to die. She knows there will not be

enough air. She knows that within me there is a '*drowned face always staring/toward the sun*'. What does it mean to drown with your face tilted toward sunlight?

14. Audrey Mestre was the no-limits record holder before Streeter. In October 2002, she attempts to reclaim her record. She is twenty-eight at the time, married to a once-brilliant older freediver, Pipin Ferreras. On an unseasonably grey day in the Dominican Republic, Mestre takes her final breath on the surface and descends on the sled. There are only two safety divers in the water with her. When she reaches her target depth of 561 feet, she pulls the pin on her compressed air bag. It does not inflate. The team on the surface wait. By the time Ferreras gets on scuba gear to help Mestre, she has blacked out. He brings her up, but she has gone without air for eight minutes and thirty-eight seconds. They attempt to resuscitate her on the surface. No doctor is present. She never regains consciousness. Some people theorise that Ferreras was jealous of Mestre's shine, that he sabotaged this dive as a convoluted means of murder.

15. There is a notice in the lobby of the leisure centre. A weekly freediving course, in the pool. This is how it will happen. I will show up and, week one, the instructor will tell me I am a natural, that I must keep coming. Week

two, they will ask me, are you sure you have never done this before, you have never breath trained? I will smile and shake my head. I am flying to the Bahamas to compete, I am a prodigy, a future record breaker. When I call to book the course, I am informed it is not suitable for under sixteens.

16. In Turkey, one summer holiday with my family, I go scuba diving. I sit at a brown school desk at the dive centre, being lectured on safety and procedure. I sign something to take responsibility for my own life. I dive off a boat, with a qualified instructor assisting me. It is hazy grey underwater. No tropical fish, no coral. I wonder why they have brought us here, whether there is nowhere better, whether maybe it was once beautiful and they had not noticed that everything beautiful had died. It is like suffocating with a tank of oxygen on my back. I try to breathe slowly, but the compressed air feels too thin. It is like being on another planet, or floating in outer space, overdressed and far from home, everyone you wanted to see has left before you arrived. The dive leaves me listless. I have never done it again.

17. Thalassophobia is the intense fear of deep bodies of water. It is not so much a fear of the water itself (aquaphobia), or specific creatures like sharks (galeophobia). There are communities of people online, sharing photos

of flooded rock quarries, underwater cliffs.
I lurk on these pages and my palms become
moist. I put my phone down on the bedside
table and dream of blue pits.

18. The Great Blue Hole, off Belize, is a marine
sinkhole that penetrates 410 feet into the
Earth's crust. From the surface, picture an
eyeball with a dilated pupil: a pale blue line
around the rim, dense black in the middle.
Under the surface, for the first 300 feet, marine
creatures thrive. Tropical fish, turtles, sharks,
coral. Below that, a layer of hydrogen sulphide
makes the water toxic, devoid of oxygen.
Nothing lives below. It is vacant black water.
On the seabed, a graveyard of conch shells.

19. Another summer, urchin shells litter the
seabed in Greece. We go on a boat trip and
stop to swim. The water is cold, impossibly
turquoise. I put on my mask and snorkel and
take a deep breath on the surface. I dive down,
root around the sea floor, bring up two, three,
four shells at a time. They are domed, delicate,
pale pastel, a hole in the middle. I give some
away and keep the rest. When we get home
I scatter them around my room, in boxes, in
drawers. Why do I have to take them? Why
is it not enough to just be there, to look, to try
and remember?

20.	But I do have to take them. Maybe, like
the orange, plastic body I once saved from
drowning, they are emblems of a far place that
I can reach. They are proof.

21.	When I turn sixteen I leave the water. I stop
swimming, and everything that is good for
me. I do things that are reckless, uninteresting.
I test my soft edges. Drink wildly, sleep in
places, with people, I should not. I try to
love somebody who floods me with himself,
wrings me out. I walk the city at night like I
own it. Wake up at the end of the bus route,
alone. Wake up smattered with lilac bruises,
no recollection why. One night, midsummer,
aged eighteen, I go out in heeled boots. I walk
home in the early hours, my footsteps echoing.
A stranger follows me. I speed up, pretend
to make a phone call. He is not deterred. Do
I keep going, past my house, so he does not
know where I live? I make a snap decision,
keys in hand. I run for my home. He follows
me up the front path. His hand on my bare leg
as I try to jab my keys in the door. I make a
guttural sound, lash out with my heeled foot.
He runs away laughing. It was just a trick, in
the end.

22.	Who were you kidding, wearing such noisy
shoes, thinking this city was yours? You are
too full of blood, of water. You are asking to
be spilled. Picture your body broken, bagged,

weighed down with bricks, tossed in a lake. When they pull you out your flesh will be wallpaper white and peeling from your face. They will tell your mother she should not see you post-mortem, she should remember you living. She will ask to see you anyway. She will recall how the smell of chlorine used to radiate from your hair when you washed it at home, no matter how hard you tried to scrub it from your scalp.

23. I take a gap year after finishing school. I do many things I later wish I had not. One of those things is gouging my foot on coral in the Pacific Ocean. I get out of the sea and laugh at the blood and then feel faint. Later that day I traipse barefoot around the island, looking for someone who might know better than me. In a small pharmacy a kind man suggests a yellow powder for the wound, to stop infection. I pack it on. I spend days in flip-flops as it heals, fading to just a pink, crescent scar. One thing I do not regret is floating on my back in the ocean at night, bioluminescent plankton swirling around me in ever-changing constellations of light.

24. A boy I meet travelling has an underwater camera. We snorkel one day and I dive down, fins on, unaware of the camera's gaze. Later he shows me a photo he took. I am alone in the blue noise, swimming through spires of

sunlight. The next day, the waterproof camera is overcome by water and stops working. Several weeks later, in a nondescript airport, the boy tells me I am a cold-blooded bitch.

25.   In the car, the first time. Five of us. Me in the middle at the back. On the M5, driving sixty, to Bristol for a friend's birthday. The rain comes down, unnoticed at first, nostalgic drum and bass submerging our ears. The rain comes down. We cannot un-notice it now. Against the windscreen, peppering our metal cage. Pinwheeling off every tyre on the motorway. The surface of the road is water. We turn the music off. We are driving sixty. Aquaplaning in a car feels like gliding, decisively, towards an ending. We fishtail into the fast lane, and back again. I cannot hear the world.

24.   It is over in seconds; my friend back in control of the wheel, hunching forward, her tears come quick. We comfort her, tell her she did everything right. The tension eases and we turn off the motorway. But my body is not mine, my palms leak water. My breath cannot penetrate my lungs the way it needs to. I say nothing. The pressure builds. It is a perverse relief, when it breaks out of me. Salt water spills down my face. My hands, my arms, buzz with nerves, go numb. This is the first time. But the problem becomes one of resurfacing: now that I know this place, can I ever really leave?

23. When we panic, our hearts begin to race. Our
    bodies, for one reason or another, interpret our
    racing hearts as an alarm. Our fear response
    sets in. A distress signal shoots from the
    amygdala to the hypothalamus, the epicentre
    of our autonomic nervous system. Our
    hormonal glands flood our bloodstreams with
    adrenaline and cortisol. The body prepares
    to escape or to defend: our pupils dilate, our
    breathing rate increases. Blood is diverted
    from extremities towards major muscle groups.
    Reflex drowns out reason. Fear is ancient, life-
    preserving. It is also a metal cage.

22. My heart is a tripwire. How do I tread
    carefully enough not to trip, but not so
    carefully that I spend my life in the shallows,
    the waves only grazing my ankles? I draw
    lines in the sand: this side yes, that side no.
    This side me, that side someone else. But the
    waves keep licking the shore. The lines can be
    moved, redrawn, and the heart can be reset.

21. I return to the water one long university
    summer. I have run too far and too often,
    run through pain, into injury. A tear in the
    cartilage of my hip socket. Whilst I wait for
    surgery, I avoid high-impact activity. The
    consultant suggests swimming to maintain
    fitness. Every morning, all summer long, I
    swim in the outdoor pool. That same leisure

centre where I first learned how to move
through water, where I watched women
inhabit their bodies. By late August, my skin
is brown from the refracted morning sunlight.
In September, I walk down a hall of operating
theatres in a hospital gown. The sounds of
surgical drilling and hammering emanate from
behind white doors. Behind my white door,
the surgeon tugs bone from socket, makes two
incisions. He stitches the inner tear and shaves
down the femoral head. He reassembles the
joint and the skin over it. I wake shivering
in the recovery room and ask for more pain
relief. It will be months before I move the way
I used to, a year before I run again.

20.   On the morning of my operation, the doctors
look with concern at a bruise on my thigh.
It is protruding from my skin, the size of a
clenched fist. Mottled blue-black with red
grazing. A couple of weeks earlier I was on
a beach in Croatia. I tried to slip smoothly
from an outcropping of rock into the cool sea,
instead I ground my leg against the rock and
tore off the top layer of skin. It burned in the
salt water, swelling within minutes. They are
unsure if they can operate with the bruise so
near my affected hip. They examine closely,
discuss quietly. Eventually I am given a nod,
and the doctor takes a marker pen and draws
a large blue arrow on my skin, avoiding the
bruise, pointing to the joint. In case there was

any doubt where to make the cut. The bruise heals, eventually, but the hair on my thigh does not grow back. The incision marks from the scalpel fade, but not entirely.

19. In Virginia Woolf's *To The Lighthouse*, on the boat off the Isle of Skye, Cam Ramsay considers the sea below her: 'About here, she thought, dabbling her fingers in the water, a ship had sunk, and she murmured, dreamily half asleep, how we perished, each alone.' I take this sentence with me. It is the final two clauses, plurality next to solitude. The absurdity of living and dying alone in a world that is full of other people living and dying alone. Woolf herself succumbs to the water, wading out into the River Ouse one night in March 1941, her pockets full of stones. One presumes she imagines the feeling beforehand. The first intake of water, the ensuing flood. In her final note to her husband, she writes: 'I know that I am spoiling your life, that without me you could work.'

18. What about the women, the girls, who do not choose submersion? In November 2017, the bodies of twenty-six Nigerian teenage girls are recovered from the Mediterranean Sea off the coast of Salerno in Italy. They are aged between fourteen and eighteen. Initial fears that they had been abused or murdered are investigated. The autopsies confirm they

each drowned, likely unable to swim when their boat, carrying them from Libya, got into trouble. Two of them were pregnant. The water treats them no differently for them having not chosen it. The water does not care that they were not taught to swim, that they left their homes behind, hoping for something better. In all press coverage of the deaths, their names do not appear. We add the shape of their watery ghosts to the nameless women we failed. We say we will do better and then we forget.

17.   But are we not all on that boat, hoping without reason or precondition, hoping that the next place will be better than this one, and the one after that even better, and so forth, until we reach the final place, where at last we will be whole? Picture a far-off island, a gently curved bay, the sea glimmering as if made of gemstones, we lie together on the softest sand. Picture your hand in mine.

16.   There are over three million shipwrecks and an estimated sixty billion dollars of precious cargo at the bottom of the sea. I save photographs of wrecks on my phone. I like the way coral grows over metal, like moss over bones. Things that should not be homes become homes anyway. Things that should not be valuable become treasure in their sinking. We seek what we have lost in the hope it will tell us how to live without it.

15. When I leave university, I travel regularly
    around the country for work with a middle-
    aged ex-cop. In the car, going from one place
    to the next, we talk about the world and about
    violence, the bad and good things people do.
    He tells me I am soft-hearted, as if it were an
    insult. As if, given a choice, I would choose
    to be otherwise. He books hotels that have
    swimming pools. He likes to swim, so I stay
    out of the water and use the gym. But I can
    see the blue pool from up here. The smell of
    chlorine still makes something echo inside me.
    One of our trips coincides with what, at the
    time, I would have called a bruised heart. It
    is August. I lie on my unfamiliar bed, white
    sheets, windows open. I watch a recent shark
    thriller on my laptop.

14. Two sisters go cage diving with great whites in
    Mexico. Their metal cage becomes detached
    from the boat and they plummet to the ocean
    floor within it. The sharks circle and their
    oxygen runs low. They stage a break for the
    surface. When I am relieved they have both
    made it up to the boat alive, I discover I
    have been experiencing a narcosis-induced
    hallucination. Only one woman makes it to
    the surface, and her mirage of a sister is killed
    by the shark. I am moved by this film. I find it
    a profound exploration of loneliness and terror
    and what our minds will do to keep our bodies
    going. I briefly forget I am bruised.

13. After that trip, I decide to watch all the shark films. In my hollow quest I come to the realisation it is not the shark itself I am looking for. It is the woman, alone, at sea. The softness of the skin, the terror of the wait on the surface. This is where the fear is: above and not below. When I realise this I lose interest in the sharks. I watch a film about two sisters trapped under the cover of a public swimming pool over a long weekend. I am not moved by it.

12. The megalodon is the largest shark that ever lived. It is estimated to be three times larger than a great white. Scientists believe it went extinct over three million years ago and our knowledge comes from fossilised teeth measuring up to seven inches in length. Despite scientific evidence of extinction, there are people who believe the megalodon still swims in our oceans. Murky online footage purports to show it alive and well, and eyewitness accounts of monster sharks and massacred whales give people hope that it lives on. We can disagree, provide evidence to the contrary, but ultimately people will simply believe what they wish. In this case, that there is something extraordinary left to find.

11. In 2013 Natalia Molchanova holds her breath for nine minutes and two seconds whilst motionless in a pool, and by August 2015 she holds forty-one freediving world records.

She gives a private dive lesson off the coast of Formentera in Spain. She is the only experienced freediver in the water, and she is diving down alone between instructional dives. Reports suggest she dives without fins to a depth of thirty-five metres. It is shallower than she would often dive but she does not account for the underwater current, the lack of supervision. She never resurfaces. The Spanish coastguard are deployed, a helicopter joins the search. Under Spanish law, a person missing at sea is presumed dead after three months.

10. The original sea women, the Japanese ama, have been diving with only their breath for over two thousand years. They begin training when they are twelve and continue diving until they are eighty or ninety. Traditionally they would dive in only a white loincloth, and a white bandana over their hair. White symbolises purity and is believed to ward off sharks. In the past they would catch seafood, until the first pearl was cultured in 1893. The Mikimoto ama collect oysters from the seabed so the pearl-producing irritant can be introduced, and then return the inseminated shells to the seabed, away from harm. They wait, for sand to become pearl, for dust to become commodity. The ama are known for their sea-whistle: the sound they make as they release breath from their lips when they resurface.

9. In some ways, London in winter could not be further from my blue-dipped horizon. In other ways, I drown all winter long. Limbs moving as if through water. Thoughts, fragmented, lost to the current. Words escaping my lips in soundless bubbles. This is the Great Blue Hole, then, the dark water without oxygen. I wade through it. I dream of ribcages pried open and shrunken hearts devoid of blood.

8. Theoretically, in the Great Blue Hole, off Belize, there is a line, above which sea life can flourish, below which it dies. It surely depends on the creature, its innate ability to withstand toxic conditions. It must be a range of lines, within which some creatures survive, with varying degrees of difficulty, and others are overcome by the conditions. There must be a line at the bottom. No creature has the faculty to survive below it. If only these creatures were sentient, and could lift each other up. If only they could reason how best to remove toxicity from the water. We do not see the graveyard on the seabed until we are falling finally towards it.

7. I retreat to my childhood home and begin to catch my breath. The healing is slow, at first. But one morning I wake and the weight of the water has left me.

6. On the Pembrokeshire coast, the summer after that winter. The hottest weekend of the year. We drive to a spot on the coast and take a precarious route to a secluded beach. We use frayed rope to clamber down a rocky ledge, get stranded in a cove. The only way out is to wade and swim, or traverse around the rock. We decide to climb. My friend goes first, she tells me it is fine, easy, not too sharp. I follow her, legs shaking. I cross my line in the sand.

5. Panic, in my fingertips first. My friend behind me tells me to get down, we will wait for the tide. But this is something I could have done. I breathe and wait for the tingling to subside. I trust my arms to hold me up, my legs to carry me. I climb around and jump into the shallows. The beach is vast, deserted, and because sunlight is bouncing off the surface of the ocean, because we are here, because the day is hot and the sea is cold, we run for the water.

4. I run for the water. I am the girl with pink shells in her hands, the woman with grey stones in her pockets. The girl being admired in the pool and the woman rotting in the changing room. A soft-hearted cold-blooded bitch, watching from the shore as they pull bodies from the sea. I meant to lie with you on the sand but I have forgotten your name again.

3. I am weightless. I am carried by the water, by the proximity of women I love. I can hear the world. I will let it in.

2. To freely place myself within blue chaos and then return to the surface. To inhabit my body. To take a breath and hold it, in the knowledge I will take another. I think it is as simple, and as complicated, as this. To go somewhere and come back again. To go somewhere with you, and both make it home again.

1. I return to the edge and find myself a child again, looking out across the blue, hoping without reason or precondition that there is something extraordinary left to find. When I close my eyes I see dark water, the reflection of stars. ▐H▌

the other side of hope

journeys in refugee and immigrant literature

autumn 2022

he other side of hope, writers are released from the narrow parameters
ected by much of the media.' The Times Literary Supplement

βλέψατε εἰς τὰ πετεινὰ τοῦ οὐρανοῦ ὅτι οὐ σπείρουσιν οὐδὲ θερίζουσιν οὐδὲ συνάγουσιν ἀποθήκας, καὶ ὁ πατὴρ ὑμῶν ὁ οὐράνιος τρέφει αὐτά· οὐχ ὑμεῖς μᾶλλον διαφέρετε αὐτῶν;

elmed by a team of refugees and immigrants, *the other side of hope* aims
challenge common perceptions of refugees ... and to chronicle the im-
grant experience.' The Bookseller

fiction · poetry · non-fiction · book reviews

Orders available on our website

othersideofhope.com

Botticelli, Sandro. *Madonna of the Sea.* c1475-80. *Wikimedia Commons.*

Apparitions, Dust

by Richard Skelton

I am looking at Botticelli's 1477 painting, *Madonna Del Mare*. Half a millennium and more has lent her skin the appearance of desiccated mud. A particular fissure runs up her chin, and another connects her nose and mouth, giving her the appearance of a hare-lip. Her head tilted slightly, her eyes expressionless, she has stared for five centuries and more over your right shoulder – or, when you are not there, into an empty room. How many faces has she seen? How many empty rooms? What is the weight, I wonder, of our cumulative gaze, and of the compounded blankness of walls and furniture? The ceaseless noise of our minds and the broad tapestries of silence. The silence of those empty rooms. The silence of the sun, tracking its days across their surfaces – across *her* surfaces. Five hundred years a moment, nothing more. A quantum perturbation in the life of a dying star. *You are all dying*, she seems to be saying, *and yet here I remain*.

Something in the absence of her gaze brings to mind countless other Madonnas I have seen in foregone days. Each of them – women and men – staring blandly out of the windows of train carriages. The ceaseless shuttle of early morning commuter traffic. Each face wearing the same

expression, head tilted slightly. Each day the
same, a repetition, distinguished only by a subtly
cycling repertoire of drab office clothing. *She
is wearing the cream blouse, it must be Tuesday. He is
wearing the chequered tie, it must be Thursday.* And so
on, into infinity. And I was one of them, watching
the passing landscape put aside the blacks and
blues of night to dress in the greens and greys of
daylight. Each morning the same. An aberrant
blur of indeterminate shapes moving past me at
speed as time itself unravelled, seeking absolution
in the maze of fields and hedgerows that stretched
ever onwards to the horizon. And all the while the
rumble and clatter, and the shrill, hypnotic squeal
of metal on metal.

What became of me? writes Pessoa, *I found myself / As one
already lost.* If I could rewrite my own history, I would
put his words in my mouth, and speak them softly,
over and over, to that lulling locomotive rhythm:
Come dimly seen, / Come, lightly felt. A chant or spell
to conjure with in the semi-darkness, as I stared
through the glass at the restless, spinning world.
   The window in Botticelli's painting is behind
his Madonna. She has turned away. The bleakness
of the landscape beyond is perhaps too much
to bear. She is the *Madonna of the Sea*, but she
has turned away. And yet, as she looks over our
shoulders, so we – or at least I – look over hers,
transfixed by the sullen intermingling of blues,
greens and yellows that somehow collude to call
themselves a landscape. A seascape. A thin, watery
wash with barely a hint of horizon. And there, in

the foreground, a ship, its sail full, taut, caught perpetually in the process of being driven onto a rocky prominence that rises improbably at the painting's edge. The towering peaks of a child's imagination. Impossibly elongated, etched in a dark and ominous blue. A calamitous fate for that solitary barque. A dire augury of the future. *Will you not look?* But she has turned away from us. She does not see us. And all the while the Saviour sits on her hip, eyeing her strangely. *You are all dying, and yet here I remain.*

Something of that scene, I feel now, years later, was played out each morning on that commuter train in the north of England. The sense each of us surely had, of being pulled towards calamity. The calamity that was the slow dismantling of our lives. Day after day. Mile after mile. Hopes, aspirations. Apparitions, dust.

'And all the while the Saviour sits on her hip, eyeing her strangely. *You are all dying, and yet here I remain.*'

I found myself as one already lost. And so I would search that black and blue landscape as it edged into daylight, looking for escape. Its indistinct smear seemed to offer something *other* than the quotidian shapes of buildings and trees, fields and hedgerows. The semi-darkness, not a limited prospect but an infinite one. A return to an oneiric space and the depthless bloom of the imagination. To dwell in dream, or at least something near to it. Unfocus your eyes. Drift.

We are moving not forwards but downwards. We are falling. Approaching escape velocity. Hearts in throats. *No.* We are floating. Our vessel approaches the Isle of the Dead. I can see the cliff's whiteness. *I can see.* I wake with a start, people eyeing me strangely. It is time to disembark.

Calamity. Days turning into weeks, into months, into years. Silt, collecting in the veins. A call centre in Manchester. Headset and cubicle. Blinkers, the narrowness of vision. It was only meant to be a stop gap, a hole-filler, a pause for reflection. *Another dirty day, another dirty dollar,* someone once said to me. Those words, ringing down the years.

Pessoa again: *A mere dream binds me to myself.* A dream of what could have been, a hope now dead. How to dream when dream itself is a rebuke? Let the river that washes us clean take not just our memories, but our dreams as well, so that, in the end, nothing remains. I would not be left with only those bitter companions. *River, run softly.* Run straight and true. Let nothing gather at your edges.

An old man accosts us on the bright lanes of our youth. I cannot see his face. He pats his chest pocket with leather hands and brings out a silver cigarette case. A war story ensues. Our eyes, our boy's quick, unfeeling eyes, looking over his shoulder for a means of escape. *Saved my life it did. Saved my life,* he says, fingering the smoothed indentation where a bullet had struck it, forty years before, ricocheting harmlessly away. Its mangled form had absorbed his death. *I wouldn't be here now. Wouldn't be here.* And we had wished him *not here*. Had wished him anywhere but here. This man, who carried an effigy of his own death in his pocket.

For children, death is something we feign, we play at, in slow motion, in mock agony, only to shake off later, with laughter. Death cannot touch us. We cannot see its face. We cannot yet hear it. *Hold your lot of years close to your chest.*

Where is it now, I wonder, that shiny, twisted talisman? Has it become an heirloom, or sold for scrap? Does it languish in some cobwebbed attic box, or has its hold on death been shaken off? Flattened, polished away to a high shine. *Hold it close. Unfocus your eyes.* What do you see in its silvered surface?

I see the River Irwell. The shared spine of two, inextricably conjoined cities, Salford and Manchester. Those call-centre years, a mist, drifting downstream.

I am disembarking the Rochdale train at Salford Central. Walking up Bridge Street. Right along Deansgate. Left onto Lloyd Street. One of a throng of people, seemingly being moved against their will. Shuttling back and forth, to and fro. At dawn and at dusk. An endlessly repeating *last walk*.

And what comes after? I think of the funeral barque Arnold Böcklin painted five times between 1880 and 1886, one for each day of the working week.

I think of that sepulchral vessel making its slow progress down the Irwell, into the Manchester ship canal, before entering the Mersey at Runcorn, past the Albert Docks and finally into the Irish Sea. And so, in this reconfiguration of the myth, the *Isle of the Dead* must be Mann, standing across some seventy-five miles of restless water to the north-west. Known to itself in Manx as *Ellan Vannin*, and Latinised as Mona's Isle, a Celtic fable marks it as the home of Mannan, otherwise known as Manannán mac Lir, sea god, and worker of the Féth fíada, the mist the Tuatha Dé Danann used to enshroud themselves, rendering their shapes invisible to human eyesight. *Blinkers, the narrowness of vision.* And Mannan shrouded not just his body, but the island itself. In this indeterminate state it is indistinguishable from the otherworldly Emain Ablach, the fabled island paradise of swans and yew trees.

One of a throng of people, seemingly being moved against their will. Shuttling back and forth, to and fro

I think again of Böcklin's painting. His trees are cypresses, not yews, but both at least are evergreen, signifying perpetuity and eternal youth. Nevertheless, Böcklin's island is impossibly small. Too small even for that rocky islet at the south-western tip of Mann, the suitably named Calf of Mann. But what about those peripheral rocks – the bane of seafarers – Kitterland, Thousla and Burroo? The latter, I discover, is known colloquially, due to its shape, as The Drinking Dragon. Crouched down, its head lies perpetually below the waves. Does it hide itself, like Mannan? Or perhaps it feeds on the souls of the dead? Those who perished at sea.

Böklin, Arnold. *Isle of the Dead*. 1883. *Wikimedia Commons*.

In Böcklin's first painting, there appears to be a coffin, athwart the prow of the boat, shrouded in a simple white cloth. In each of the subsequent four renderings of the scene this winding sheet is garlanded, removing all doubt, should there have been any, as to its purpose. But there is still mystery here. In addition to the boatman, there is another figure, presiding over the coffin, also cloaked in white. One of these two figures must be a psychopomp, whose role is to escort the souls of the newly dead to their place of eternal rest. In Classical mythology it is the boatman himself, Charon, who fulfils this function, but Böcklin's oarsman at the stern of the boat seems a marginal figure, painted in drab colours. Perhaps this very indeterminacy – the figure seems to fade into the background in the last three versions of the painting – is apt for the adumbral role of death's escort. It is as if Böcklin has used the substance of shadows themselves as his medium.

And if the boatman is half-cloaked in darkness, then the figure presiding over the coffin is, by comparison, near luminous. Such brightness is fitting for the role of guide, counsellor, guardian, and if each painting is viewed in sequence, then the figure appears to slowly tilt its head forward, until, in the last painting, it is half-bent over the coffin, as if performing some last office, or simply rousing the sleeping soul. *Wake up. It is time to disembark.* But another interpretation might suggest that the white figure is the newly dead soul itself, which, as it approaches this last shore, stoops to take leave of its corporeal form, before voyaging onwards, alone.

The journey onwards. Day after day. Year after year. High whine of metal on metal as the brakes are applied and the train carriage comes to rest. A disembodied voice announces the station. *Manchester Victoria.* This time I have slept too long. Salford Central is behind me. Where is my guide to this, my own private Isle of the Dead? A place not of blessed repose but damnation. In this heretic reconfiguration of the myth, the *Island's* northern banks are bounded by the Irwell, whilst the Rochdale Canal forms its southerly perimeter, the two waterways converging, momentarily, in the labyrinth of channels and basins near the old Hulme Locks. This slender noose cast around the city's neck is tightened by a phantasmal offshoot of the Islington Marina, which runs north-west up Bengal Street, bisecting the Community Fire Station before continuing up Gould Street, where it joins the last reaches of the River Irk as it empties into the Irwell below Victoria Station.

But something presses against my chest. I cannot move my hands. I watch the others slowly depart

Victoria, again. *Wake up. It is time to disembark.* But something presses against my chest. I cannot move my hands. I watch the others slowly depart. *Don't leave me here,* I would say, if I could move my lips. *Don't leave.*

I found myself as one already lost. A recurrent dream
from childhood. I am walking with my parents
down a quiet country lane. My eye is caught
momentarily by something in the hedgerow – a
wayward glance, nothing more – but when I look
back down the road, my parents are gone. I look
to the far hills, and through some trick of dream-
perspective I see them. Impossibly far away, and yet I
know it is them. Mother, father, and alongside them
a third, smaller figure. Passing over the horizon.
Who is the third who walks always beside you? Eliot
writes in *The Waste Land*, conjuring Shackleton's
experience of 'things intangible' among the glaciers
of South Georgia in 1917 – an experience shared by
his companions, Worsley and Crean, on that last,
delirious thirty-six-hour trek. *It seemed to me often that
we were four, not three*, writes Shackleton, and Worsley
confesses to a *feeling* that *there was another person with
us.* A spectral companion.

Eliot transforms this extra-corporeal sense into
something seen, or at least half-seen:

> When I count, there are only you and I together
> But when I look ahead up the white road
> There is always another one walking beside you
> Gliding wrapt in a brown mantle, hooded
> I do not know whether a man or a woman
> – But who is that on the other side of you?

A figure, barely discerned, shrouded, mute. Like
Tiresias, or the cloaked white form in Böcklin's
paintings, a persona of indeterminate gender. An

attendant presence, gliding through the gamut of fixed forms without ever dwelling in one. And, like the Pleiades, only apprehended with averted vision – a wayward glance – both revealed and occluded at the same time.

How to approach those that hover at the edges of our perception? I need no such sleight-of-hand vision to apprehend my dream *other* – that third, smaller figure walking beside my parents. In each repetition of the dream I see it with preternatural clarity. It wears my own child's shape. Has someone else – something else – taken my place, my semblance, while I looked away? *No.* In those brief moments a blade slipped between us, and I was cut adrift from myself, untethered.

At every allotted break, during those call-centre years, I leave the office on Lloyd Street and make my way towards the river. I am looking for something. Drawn to the riddle of back streets behind Deansgate: *Saint Mary's St to Southgate to King Street to Dunlop St to Garden Ln to Smithy Ln to King St W to Saint Mary's Parsonage.* Circling, round and round. And the river always near and yet impossibly far, hidden behind an impenetrable vertical barrier of concrete, brick and slate. Its primordial drone drowned out by the city's hum.

We are moving not forwards but downwards. Into the chthonic city. Look behind the façades, the dazzling frontages, the glass and lacquer. Here in the alleyways there is no effort at disguise, no subterfuge. Bloated chain stores and diminutive local businesses converse on equal terms, in a language of rust, peeling paint and crumbling masonry. Perhaps there is a clue here. Following the elliptical logic of Eliot's poem, to *look ahead up the white road* of the high street is to see, peripherally, *another* city, down the side streets. And it walks darkly with us, hooded and obscured, as we walk along those avenues of light.

| **Bloated chain stores and diminutive local businesses converse on equal terms, in a language of rust, peeling paint and crumbling masonry**

And I cannot help but lose myself. Wandering a waking dream. A dream in which my vision is perpetually veiled, seeking, perhaps, traces of my soul's passage, always ahead of me, and out of sight. Five hundred years a moment, nothing more. A quantum perturbation in the life of a dying star. ⊞

References
Eliot, T.S. *The Waste Land*. Faber and Faber Ltd (1922)
Pessoa, Fernando. 'Scaffolding' and 'Excerpt from an Ode'. *Selected Poems* (translated by Peter Rickard). Edinburgh University Press. (1971). Translated lines from both poems used with the permission of the Estate of Peter Rickard.
Shackleton, Ernest. *South: The Endurance Expedition*. Heinemann (1999)

How to Care

for a Rose

by Laura Dobson

Choose the location carefully

I rank my options in a colour-coded spreadsheet.

I'm reluctant to risk another house share. Having deferred my final year, I know next to no one. When I select a studio flat, both parents accompany me to collect the keys. A student loan will cover most of my rent; they'll help with the rest.

Little L, this is lovely.

A month has passed since my younger brother graduated – BA(Hons) Jurisprudence – in Oxford's Sheldonian Theatre; the opening proceedings delivered in spoken Latin, champagne toasts in the college quad, sensing I'd been dismissed as furniture once I mumbled *Nottingham Trent* and *Fashion Design*.

Mmm.

We visit a local supermarket and I stock up for the coming term; a palette of pigments dresses the doorway. I buy the miniature rose on an impulse, prop it between tinned soup and a three-kilogram bag of fusilli for the drive back to the flat. We haul bags for life up the four flights of stairs.

The yellow blooms brighten my table for one,
clenched buds concealed beneath every flower.
We should get going. Dad glances at his watch.
It'll be OK, love. Mum clasps, then releases my hand.
After they leave, I dampen the soil directly
from the tap. The sound is a swarm; it rises to a
crescendo within the pipework. I notice an extractor
that will hum night after night.

Plant properly to help the roots to become established

Practised in setting up home in new-to-me spaces, I
make my bed first. I seek comfort in worn duck-egg-
blue sheets but I'm reminded of scalding spilt mint
tea and questionable choices.

Hearing the clatter of a wheeled suitcase, I rush
to the door. I glimpse the arriving tenant through
the peephole. Shoulder-length waves. A studded
leather jacket. I move away.

I roll knickers into cylindrical parcels and
progress to socks, folding the top of one over the
top of its partner before tucking both inside the
pocket created. A sea-toned mosaic forms within the
drawer; I nudge it shut.

Every kitchen utensil and item of crockery is a
scuffed shade of turquoise.

I arrange my books in height order. Tallest is *The
Royal Horticultural Society Encyclopaedia of Plants and
Flowers*, proudly purchased – at age thirteen – with
a book token awarded for academic attainment.
I'd just visited the Malvern Flower Show and
discovered Aquilegia.

My Kennett and Lindsell mannequin, and roll of cotton calico, take longest to house. I tuck them beside the wardrobe where they're least obtrusive.

Finally, battery-powered fairy lights, frames of family photographs, Lucinda bear, pyjamas. I brush my teeth with fennel paste and massage lavender into my pulse points.

When removing dead blooms, slice cleanly at a 45° angle

Treat this year as a full-time job and you'll be fine, the tutor announces in our first lecture. I settle into a routine of nine-to-five days.

On the twenty-fourth of November, my phone rings as I'm returning to my flat. It's Dad; he explains that one of our cats has been unwell. He took her to see a vet — *your mum and I didn't see this coming either* — brought her home for burial. The path back from campus is steep; it drops away.

Darling, I really am sorry. We know how much you loved her.

I pass no one in the lobby, on the staircase, in the corridor. I think of Gin, now sole survivor of her rescued litter, picture the yang-shaped space beside her that was Tonic. The pair have curled up together, tail to nose, for seventeen years. Their bellies rising, falling: two lungs breathing as one.

I know, love. I hang up. My insides growl.

I boil a small pan of water and let it simmer.

The serrated knife slices easily through the plastic packet, scatters spaghetti before it pierces my left thumb. Crimson spurts from a knuckle-width incision, seeps into day-old washing-up water and becomes an ocean. The wound gapes open. As I fumble to stem the flow, the room swims.

I smear the screen as I dial.

Mum, it won't stop bleeding. How do I know if I need stitches? What if I pass out?

Fertilise regularly to ensure a slow, steady supply of nutrients

When the combination microwave oven fails to be either, I visualise bacteria multiplying within me, conjure an image that more closely resembles sticky-fingered toddlers flowing through the tubes and chambers of soft play than a biologically accurate diagram. Twelve years have passed since I was routinely weighed and measured: an outlier plotted well beneath the curve.

> **Twelve years have passed since I was routinely weighed and measured: an outlier plotted well beneath the curve**

Make sure you're eating properly, L.

Mum, I will.

I coax myself through swallowing a forkful of lukewarm moussaka, peppery and pungent. I've no idea what food poisoning smells like; still, my nostrils flare to assert danger. I pick up the plate, splatter the bin liner with the remains. Retch.

Later, I read about the Eastern concept of Xushi (emptiness-substance). As I consider the equal importance of what is absent and what is present, hunger pangs intrude. I crunch through tortilla chips, then slice away sections of printer paper with a scalpel.

22:34
Mum, could you scan the Chinese paper-cuts you brought back from Jinan?
I've had an idea for my final project x
22:36
Love, there are hundreds of them. I'll send a few.
Goodnight, sleep well x

I continue into the early hours, soon guiding the blade through printed images: abstract florals, human faces. The cuts are intuitive and I find rhythm, release. I take more and more away, fascinated by what remains. As I experiment, tessellating shapes to create a series of geometric lattices, my desk becomes buried under a flurry of offcuts.

Allow a rest period during winter
I am a snow globe shaken into chaos, shaken again before the flakes can settle. I aspire to lay fresh tracks; instead, I endure a biting, blinding journey through the blizzard.

I am a snow globe shaken into chaos, shaken again before the flakes can settle

I develop an ocular migraine. Visual rain dances across my computer screen, vying for attention with the text of my dissertation underneath. I revisit, replace, and still find fault with each word, my every thought already eloquently expressed by an experienced researcher.

Beyond my window, a Christmas market sprawls
– merry – across the square; its string-lit stalls
taunt. Mulled wine and bratwurst, aromatherapy
oils, skewered fruit, fleece-lined bobble hats. Carols
blare on loop; carousel horses go in circles.
Four times, I rewrite my fourth chapter, unable
to reach a meaningful conclusion.
I'm impatient to see it in print.

—

When I venture out to collect a proof copy,
a bittersweet breeze carries cinnamon and
clementine. Still to finalise the line-up for my
graduate collection – others have begun to draft
paper patterns – I continue to the studio, bound
book in hand.
   Oh my God, *let me see! As if, Laura. It looks so
professional. Will you read through mine before I get it printed?*
She knows my name from our weekly tutorial.
   Sure. I'll write down my email.
   We could maybe go to the library now?
   Sure, OK.

Ensure that your rose has sufficient water
The Bagua octagon is used in Feng Shui to restore
harmony. Sky, earth, thunder, wind, water, fire,
mountain, and lake are the fundamental principles
of reality it is seen to represent. An integral concept,
like Xushi; I reference this in each of my garments.
I title the project 'Balance'.

Meanwhile, I move from hand rendered to digitised designs. What began as a series of botanic paint splatters becomes a sublimation print. I smooth out shaky pencil lines on screen, programme a laser beam to carve out my pattern pieces, accurate to ± 0.0005 inch.

Days merge. I spend eight hours in the studio, then eight more in my flat. My first garment is a short and short-sleeved trapeze dress with eight panels. Teal cotton; I construct a first final version from paper silk but deem it lacklustre. The pin hem alone is a day's work.

A technical drawing is required for my graduate portfolio; I map out the silhouette, then consider each seam line and pipe fold. An octagonal protrusion elevates the right shoulder. Using the pen tool, I click to plot points, hold and drag to define curves. Next, the lattice overlay. I estimate a thousand cut-out shapes and strive to capture the natural drape of each one. In flow state, I don't drink anything or use the toilet. I begin the illustration at 10pm. It's just after 6am when I finish.

Pride courses through me. This is what I'm capable of.

I sleep for just one hour. Bleary-eyed yet alert, I return to the studio without breakfast to guarantee I'll find space. Already, a dozen machines pound like a charging herd.

Avoid pruning during growing season
You're starting your sketchbook again? Now? But why? I've done so twice already.

This time, the spiral-bound book I've chosen is square. For a few minutes, there is only potential in its pages. I transfer three sketches across, everything else into the bin; at once, it might have been better to work on loose-leaf cartridge paper. The final hand-in looms. I've a garment still to make. I compete with the laser cutter's mechanised precision. The industrial sewing machine is temperamental; the needle stutters and jolts. Each time I unpick a strayed seam, I'm left with tiny holes, messy traces of severed cotton thread.

‖ Alone in my flat, I study the perforations, confused when they appear perfectly parallel

Over and over, the panels come together and then apart.

Alone in my flat, I study the perforations, confused when they appear perfectly parallel.

Time runs out. My trench coat is in pieces.

—

A chipped plastic crate houses my year's work: my sketchbook, graduate portfolio, final garments, specification sheets and paper patterns. Digital files on labelled USB sticks. Fabric samples. My heart. My soul. My dissertation: *An Investigation into the Possibility and Importance of Creating Emotionally Durable Products Through Emotionally Significant Processes.*

The deserted workspace is all right angles and sharp edges. I scan alphabetised names for my designated spot and set the box down. Lidded, largely indistinguishable from another seventy-nine, it awaits scrutiny.

I leave at once, scarcely able to stem tears; I expected that I'd feel lighter.

Skimming the top of the tallest buildings is a line, ruler straight and the shade of sunlight on a magnolia wall. Above, an expanse of flat grey resembles poured concrete. The band below sparkles like blue calcite. I walk towards it but it remains distant, unreachable. I have a sense that it always will.

Resuming good care may help your rose to recover

Little L, how are you getting on? We'll be there around lunchtime.

Almost done.

Crammed suitcases, holdalls and jute bags are assembled along one wall. The crate waits with them, lid firmly in place. Years will pass before I'm ready to unpack it.

I walk towards it but it remains distant, unreachable. I have a sense that it always will

The milk in my fridge has long expired. I try not to gag as it glugs down the sink.

A silicone ice cube tray, obtained from the freshers' fayre and lent out to make vodka jelly, has got pushed to the back of an otherwise emptied cupboard. I expected to emerge from university as a fully formed adult; instead, I feel fluid and ill-defined.

I crouch to retrieve it, add the marine blue mould to a box marked 'kitchen'.

I strip my bed last. The fitted sheet folds into itself.

With a microfibre cloth, I disinfect each surface until it smells citrus fresh and forgets me. In three months, the flat will have another occupant. I don't know where or who I'll be.

My phone buzzes. I locate it on the table beside the ceramic plant pot. The email alert is early. I inhale and count slowly to six, then click through to the university portal and log in.

We expected nothing less, my grandparents remark when I call to tell them. Expected.

I scoop up skeletal remains but leave with first-class honours. **H**

And Who Would I Then Have Been?

by Ali Seegar

October 1984

You need to sign here.' The woman pushes the open ledger across the desk, using her biro to indicate the space for my signature. 'Don't worry, it's standard,' she continues, seeing me fumble for the pen, 'we need to keep a record of our conversation.' She turns back to the electric typewriter, feeds through a trio of carbon-copy paper and starts to type.

Slipping my hand off the desk, I wrap it around my stomach where it feels warmer and safer and sit for a moment wondering why, after remaining calm throughout the twenty-minute interview, my nerves now betray me. My lip, caught between my teeth, is chewed red raw. Taking a deep breath, I release it slowly. Which doesn't help at all. The only thing I'm certain of is uncertainty setting in.

Only an hour ago, I'd been so sure about coming here. Hanging onto the metal pole as I rode the double-decker down Kingsway, sounds of the Style Council plugged into my ears; leaving behind the conductor's calls of 'idiot' as I jump off before Aldwych when the bus slows at a red light; weaving my way past pedestrians to St Catherine's House. Births and Marriages Indexes, that's what I would find there. One birth in particular – mine.

Of course, I'd not spent my whole life wondering who I was and from where I came. Tucked away in a small village in Kent, my childhood had passed relatively carefree with a mother, father, brother and array of different-sized dogs. I can't even remember the day I was told about my adoption; my parents were encouraged to use that word, so it became something familiar, not scary. I do remember my brother and me being taken into the sitting room one day, each seated on a knee and told something significant. It could have been about our adoptions, or some news equally important to a seven- and eight-year-old, like the summer holiday being cancelled. I do remember soon afterwards telling my mother she didn't love me, and then running away down the farmer's lane until I reached the T-junction where the egg-lady lived. Sitting under the white wooden signpost, I'd not wanted to go further but was afraid to go back. Then my mother turned up in our bright blue Beetle and took me to Hever Castle for tea and cake.

Curiosity kicked in as I got older, I suppose. And it was clear to anyone who knew anything about genetics there was something strange about my blue eyes and fine mousey hair that were the chalk or the cheese to the rest of the household. Then eighteen hit. Legally, I could now ask for my birth certificate and, provided I could prove I was not insane, would be given it. No more questions asked.

But questions are why I have come to St Catherine's House.

And why today is so important. Why I've put on a dress and bunked off college. And why the

woman before me – the psychiatrist I've spent all
these minutes convincing I won't be knocking on
my birth mother's door with an axe in my hand –
mustn't see me falling apart.

Everything's speeding up and slowing down simultaneously because it's clear something monumental is happening...

Hearing the metallic whirl of the typewriter wheel,
I look up. The woman takes the papers, signs them,
then folds the top copy and puts it into an envelope. My
tongue plays with the bump on my lip from where I've
been biting it. Realising I haven't yet signed the ledger,
I quickly lean forward and scrawl. She smiles at me. I
try smiling back but my mouth feels tight. Everything's
speeding up and slowing down simultaneously because
it's clear something monumental is happening; because
written on the paper now stuffed in the envelope is
the means to my identity. She puts the letter on the
desk and slides it towards me.

'You'll need to show this when you collect your
certificate in three days' time,' she says in the
unembellished tone of a newsreader.

The words smack like a fist into my stomach.
My search is starting, that I know. I mean, I hadn't
expected my birth mother to pop up shouting
'surprise' when I entered the psychiatrist's office
– but waiting another three days when I've waited
months for this appointment feels unbearable. I
swallow my disappointment and nod. Then she says,

'Would you like to know your name?' and I
think, *but I know my name*. Then I realise she doesn't

mean *my* name. She means my other name. The
one I'd been called for the first six weeks of my life.
And a part of me wonders if I can ever go back to
being *me* once I know who I might have been. And
I wonder if I'd have liked myself more if I'd been
that other me. And a torrent of questions races
through my head and I wonder how many I will
find answers to, once I know that baby's name. And
I nod. She places another folded sheet on top of the
envelope and sits back in her chair.

The paper feels thick and smooth and scrunches
lightly as I unfold it. My eyes skim the lines of legal
text, but I let them fade before me, until two words
remain – Julia Rolt. The ones belonging to me.

Nineteen eighty-four. October. Britain reels like a
drunkard from the Brighton bombing twelve days
ago. Wham! tops the charts with their anthem to
freedom, while the world is shocked into action with
the BBC's footage of 'a biblical famine' in Ethiopia.

Rewind some eighteen years earlier, however,
and you will reach an unseasonably mild afternoon
in early March, when my mother enters this story.

She is baking bread – so she has told me
– floured up to her elbows, when the phone rings.
Hurrying to the dining room, she picks up the
receiver of the beige Bakelite phone hanging on the
wall by the window seat.

'Speaking,' she replies, in answer to the caller's
question.

The woman gives her name and where she is
calling from. After exchanging pleasantries, she

apologises. It is unusual for the adoption agency to make early contact, she says, but an opportunity has arisen. Feeling her legs weaken at the news, my mother gropes for the window seat and sits. Sixteen months ago, she had sat on the same seat talking to the same woman and the result – she looks over at the toddler asleep by the French windows – was her son.

Now there is another baby. A girl this time. The woman apologises again, saying that she knows my parents don't want to adopt another child yet, but this baby's mother is a pianist. The agency had agreed it was a perfect match.

When I first heard this story, I would imagine my mother sitting on the window seat. Sometimes, I would sit there myself pretending to be her being told about me. As I got older, though, it was the woman on the line I would obsess about, wondering who she was and with whom she had discussed me before making that call. I would imagine her taking some other file from her cabinet, dialling another number, speaking to a different, desperate couple. What if my mother had been out or my parents away? Would she have persisted until she reached them or taken her marker and crossed out their name? Was it fate? Chance? Sheer luck that landed me the life I have been living ever since?

My mother would tell me how grateful she was for the agency's peccadillo because it gave her me. If that call had come eight months later – the two-year gap between adoptions my parents had initially decided upon – then someone else would have been her daughter. Someone else, a few months younger than I, would be walking around with my name. And who then would I have been?

Sometimes people ask if I mind being adopted, which is a strange question because who is willingly removed from their natural family unless, of course, there is an underlying necessity. But as I only know the life I've had – for which I would like to point out I am extremely fortunate to have been given – it's a question I don't know how to answer. How can I compare my life with the one it might have been when I don't know what it would have been? I'm reminded of Robert Frost's poem *The Road Not Taken*, only it was the woman in the agency, not me, who decided which path I should take.

> **Someone else, a few months younger than I, would be walking around with my name. And who then would I have been?**

After leaving the psychiatrist's office, it feels impossible to step back into the busy world outside. Instead, I find myself wandering the main hall of St Catherine's House feeling, if anything, rather discombobulated, smaller than when I had woken this morning, unsure of myself. The place is cathedral vast, my footsteps muffled by the multitudinous bookshelves groaning with blood-red volumes as thick as my palm. Contained within each are thousands of names and dates and places. Babies born. People wed. I feel them staring though their leather-bound spines at me. Millions of my fellow countryfolk. Are they daring me towards aisle 1966? To the book embossed Jan-Mar 1966? I tread softly, afraid to wake their spirits, and arrive instead at a corner tucked away to the right where the bookshelves are smaller, the tomes midnight-blue and the word Adoptions replaces Births. It feels easier here, more familiar. I know who I will find.

It doesn't take me long to locate myself amongst the lines of unwanted yet longed-for babies. A few words: my name, birth date and place of registration. Nothing connecting me with Julia. Carefully, I close the book and return it to its rightful place.

Time to leave but still my feet won't walk me through the door. Instead they carry me steadfastly back into the bowels of the hall, hurrying me towards the 1960s as if, now I've found my adoption, I must confirm my birth. Around me, people drift down the aisles staring hawklike at books or stand scribbling notes beside an open tome. I reach 1964 where somewhere on the shelves my brother's first identity awaits should he wish to know. Electricity sparks at my fingertips as I run them along the countless books of babies; shelf after shelf of them neatly alphabetised and stored by the year's four quarters.

Before realising, I'm past '65 and standing by '66. My fingers leave ghost trails as I walk slowly past Carringtons and Carys, Harrisons and Hays. Arriving at the last third of the alphabet, I slacken my pace. My eyes flit like a hunter's eyes until they settle on the book I seek.

It's heavy and bulky. Cradling it tight to my chest, swaddling it in my arms, I make my way to an empty lectern. A memory flashes past as I place the book down. Nine, ten years old, reading the sixth lesson at a carol service, a lump in my throat the size of this volume, rabbit-dazed silent as the congregation stare expectantly. They are surrounding me now, all of them, in these books. Anticipation waits weighted. I open the cover to retrieve my life.

Robert, Roberts, Robertso, Robertson. I'm dizzy with surnames but still I keep going; through Rolles and Rollestons now. Turning the page, I run my finger down the left side, stop, reverse slightly and there I am. Sandwiched between Rolstone, Brian and Roma, Anthony.

ROLT

JULIA   **ROLT**   **LAMBETH**

The words leave the page, running through my hand, up my arm, through my veins until, tumbling in waves of anger and sadness and guilt, they reach my heart. So much guilt. I think about my parents, their love for me, what they have given me. Am I betraying them, wanting to know more? I don't want to be anyone but me. But I can't go back now. I can't. I must find the woman whose surname I bore, who bore me in her womb. Who gave me life, then gave me up. Why? Why didn't she want me?

Slowly, I close the book, allowing its secrets to slumber again. In three days, I'll return. My journey will continue. But for now, I must be patient. ∎

HINTERLAND
GIVE THE GIFT OF
CREATIVE NON-FICTION

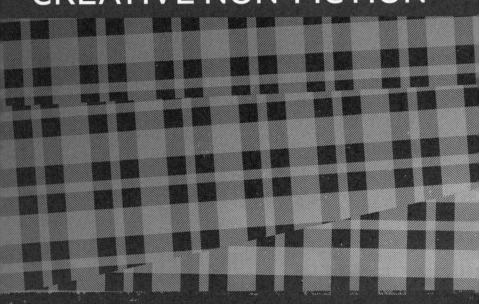

SUBSCRIPTIONS AND GIFT BUNDLES
AVAILABLE FROM OUR WEBSTORE,
GIFT-WRAPPING SERVICES AND
PERSONALISED MESSAGES
AVAILABLE ON REQUEST

WWW.HINTERLANDNONFICTION.COM

Eating Cornflakes

with Patrick Moore

by Dave Wakely

I am the third character in this story.
I have a name, but it is mostly only whispered.
The professionals skirt around me, refer to me as
'the condition'.
Other people, the ones like you, usually think of
me as fog. Something swirling and opaque that
obscures and mystifies. I am not so romantic.
Fog conceals us, but it does not dissolve: it burns
away in morning sun, revealing the world afresh.
I linger while the people evaporate.
I am never welcomed, but I will
introduce myself. My name is
Vascular Dementia. You may call
me VaD.
But think of fog if that's easier.
Familiarity is comforting.
You'll be wanting that.

Misty mornings here,
walking the dog on
the cliffs. We can
hear the foghorns,
but can't see any ships.
Postcard from my mother,
1987

———

I don't usually remember so far back clearly, but on 22 November 1990 I was in bed with flu. When the phone rang, I groped about sleepily to answer it.

'That fucking bitch has finally gone,' said a jubilant female voice. Instantly, I knew three things.

Firstly, my mother was calling. Unlike my father, she would never be mistaken for the well-modulated precision of Radio 4. Not with those adjectives.

Second, Margaret Thatcher had either died or resigned. I crossed some fingers.

And third, a celebration was called for.

Lemsip and vodka ahoy.

—

Fifteen years later, something else fiercely made-up came madly undone. My mother's mind.

Prime Ministers aren't the only things that come unstuck. Even the most determined glue dries out with age. The reliably definite becomes the cautiously conditional, the limb you avoid going out on that might no longer take your weight.

The literal and the abstract wore each other's clothes. The dictionary's definitions became loose-leaf, randomly shuffled at each attempt to tidy them. She'd always called a spade a spade but she didn't know the word for what she needed now, and neither did I.

—

The forgiving flexibility of neighbourly kindness reached its limits in the autumn of 2005. The crunch came with a yellow duster. The house-proud love to clean and polish, but a neighbour's kerbstone buffed past midnight by a woman who's locked herself out for the third time in two days doesn't speak of thoughtfulness.

Across the river, ghosts of the dead stalk Hampton Court Palace. On the southern bank, a ghost of the living walks a dog and chatters with half-familiar strangers.

Friends rally, unbidden. Every morning, though I have no shortage, they generously bring me fresh concerns.

—

Morning David, we had a long chat last night. She was very upset about all the people in her house, especially the gypsies in the bathroom.
Neighbour's email, 2005

The following day, I poured afternoon tea. The elastic of family had s t r e t c h e d as far as Buckinghamshire, wound around my ankle and snapped me back to childhood. The sun glinted on a teaspoon poking through grape hyacinths.

The cat chased butterflies among pansies thrust into soil container and all, pot rims proud like battlements. I ran after words like a giddy sheepdog: son, mother, father, husband...

Their meanings scattered every time I rounded them up. It was like drawing diagrams in moving water, pointing at the moon for a cat. *(Try it. The cat will look at your finger.)*
For twenty or more years, she'd been a relative stranger, but now the words drifted apart: a relative. And a stranger... One minute I was her husband's father, next I was her husband. Soon my father was my brother, and then her father. Then she'd never been married but I, a widow's only child, had brothers.

Within weeks, VaD would be throwing chairs across psychiatric wards, hurling teacups and insults. Mum would be a woman possessed. It got easier when we knew who by. And there was 'the other David' she kept asking about. Not my partner, although sharing a name didn't help. A younger man, soft-spoken and idealistic, carrying a violin case. 'He never visits: have you seen him?' Only in photographs, Mum. I stopped being him thirty years ago.

—

She has remembered to go shopping. In the fridge, there are tomatoes – red (fresh) and green (furry) – six pounds of cheddar, four packs of butter, a pair of socks and a hat. Her head is obviously hot. Perhaps she is feverish.

—

When they're not thinking about
fog, people think of me as being
like an escalator. A slow ramp
d$_{o}$w$_{n}$ $_{i}$n$_{t_{o}}$...
            well, pick a word.
What scares you most?
I do not dance with old ladies
at twilight. I don't take their
hands and slide them down the
banisters.
I push them down the st$_{ai}$$_{rs}$.
In the dark. Once in a while, an unexpectedly
                                  large
step down. No warnings, no markings.

*Sentences stammer
like warped records,
the stylus skipping to
and fro. Songs become
unbearable, CDs
wrenched from the
player when they start. I
listen to* Some Day It Will
Please Us To Remember
Even This, *hide my copy
of* Stop Making Sense.

The Community Psychiatric Nurse calls it bungy
jumping without the river. She texts him.
'Mum dropped again. Dipped head in concrete.
No bounce.' He understands perfectly.

—

Clockwork. That was how things ran. Tick tick tick... But
clockwork runs down. Loses momentum, loses moments.
Time carried on but the numerals
floated free from the clock face,
absconded. The left hand forgot what
the right hand was doing. She washes the
newspapers and reads the tea towels.

*I keep my own
timetable.
"At the third
stroke ..."*

—

Once she sewed and knitted, needles clacking like
castanets. Now I unpick her embroidery, uncover
the seamstress among the pleats of
I am the nail her history. Her hems are freshly
on which she is snagged. pressed, but she drags a train of
dangling threads.
For her every stitch,
I drop two. —

At eight o'clock, she put detergent
in the cat's bowl and put the cat in the laundry basket.
Then she napped. At 11pm, she asked what I wanted for
breakfast. We watched *The Sky At Night*, ate cornflakes
with Patrick Moore. Later, we watched Teletext. 'I don't
like these subtitled films,' she said.

—

They hide things. She hides money in the cistern,
teapots in the coal bunker. He hides the truth from
her and his feelings from himself.
I make them lose things too. Her keys. His
concentration. Her middle ages. His job.
I hide her memories in a glass jar, give her a pickle
fork and a blindfold. They work together: a bonding
exercise. Every time she retrieves a memory, I make
the jar a little smaller.

—

She phones cabs in the middle of
the night, asks to be taken to a home
that multiplies and divides, scattering
itself across South London. VaD
parcels her for re-delivery, 'no longer
known at this address'.
'Home' – or a home, at least – is
where we put her last week. It's not
the word she uses to describe it.

Anti-psychotics?
Of course, if you think
they will help.
Where do I sign?

Oh, for her. I see...

—

We spent two hours
with Mum last night.
She wasn't in.

'It's nice here, but they're all mad,'
she says, glassy-eyed and grinning.
Yet she's kind to them all.
We take her Christmas presents and
she distributes them fondly to those that have none.
She remains selfless, although the definition has changed.

—

I have been stalking her for a while. Mugging, they
called me the first time. Only with the bruise to her
forehead and her purse untouched on top of her
open bag.

—

I sew her name into Little by little, things get harder to
knickers and bras, manage. Radios drift from channels
the inside of slippers. like unmoored boats, controls
They still get lost, become remote. The home's collie
unrecognised. refuses to be a Norfolk terrier, never
I should sew labels answers to 'Honey'. She tries to
of my own. Partner, replace me with my younger self. He
editor, cook, son. fails to arrive.
Things can so easily 'Broken', she says. She doesn't
go astray. specify the noun.

—

The second time I was called Fainting. She stepped
off the kerb and into the chasm. I treated her
like royalty, crowned her with a Bentley's bonnet
emblem as she fell. Stupid little accident, she said.
One of my specialities.

—

As VaD backspaces through her autobiography, I
build sandbanks of photo albums to shore up leaky
recollections. I fill in names and places, re-captioning
memories so she can forget them afresh.

—

The third time, they racked her brain for clues. Small
vessel disease, they called me then. But no indication
of the height of the waves or the direction of the tide.

Time flies backwards. Early in 2006,
the Second World War breaks out.
The carers text me.
'1941,' they say. I call back, puzzled.
'Not *the* time: *her* time,' they tell me.
'Visit early. She's worried about the
air-raids.'
She describes the smoke over
Clapham as dawn broke and the
suffocating smell of the gas mask. A
friend has brought Mum's dog to see her. A dog she will
not own for fifty years and cannot identify. My friend's
daughter, preparing for History GCSE, listens as the
Pathé Newsreels scroll through Mum's head. The little
table in the Anderson shelter, the primroses by its door,
overnight damage in Balham. She is still disposed to
teach, to protect. She pours tea, eager to be mother.

*9pm in a
Buckinghamshire
marketplace as deserted
as curfew.
I scan the night sky for
doodlebugs, anxious to
get home and listen for
All Clear.*

—

We were separated at birth. She tubercular, me untimely
ripped. For thirteen weeks I lay in an incubator, waiting
to be held. For ten years, she took me to doctors to
check my spine was straightening. For forty-six years, the
cause of problems, held at a distance.
She describes a street I knew as a child, accurate to the
individual trees. Minutes later, two years since diagnosis,
she tells me she loves me for the first time. I am forty-
seven. We have taken the winding road, but perhaps we
have reached the truth.

—

I WILL WEAVE MY MOTHER A COSY BLANKET

Her world is smaller every day. Down to just four walls, a rug, a hand basin. There is no room left for anxieties, for yesterday or tomorrow. Now there is just the single moment. We fill the remaining spaces with warmth: with hot tea, chocolate cake, hugs. She is teaching us to live in the here and now ...

FROM LITTLE WHITE LIES AND OMMISSIONS THAT SHE MIGHT DRAPE AROUND HERSELF TO SPARE HER THE CHILL

—

Drawer by drawer, they empty the house of all those things she stashed away for rainy days or safekeeping. For any emergency except this.
He takes his upbringing to charity shops or gives it away to friends.
Yesterdays slide away like a train at an adjacent platform. Earlier versions of her crowd its seats: the skinny bride who made the cricket teas, the housewife who passed home-baked cake over the fence to neighbours. As they pull away in the other direction, he half-believes for a moment he is moving forward.

—

It's like visiting a little girl
who wants to stay up
and talk but is too tired
to get the words out.
Like watching a toy
whose batteries are
almost out of juice.
Email to a friend,
February 2008

My little girl is seventy-nine. I brush the muffin crumbs from her dressing gown and comb her hair. I'm privileged. The only man she will allow to touch her. She ignores her husband's photo on the shelf, says she'd like to marry one day. When she's older.

My old Mum is five, maybe six. It's my turn now: to tuck her into bed, to put away the toys. To deal with scrapes and shoo away the bullies.
I am the son and father now. She is the unholy ghost.

—

Broken. My favourite word.
The first time, I lure her from bed to visit the people in the cellar I have dug in her imagination.
I conjure an orchestra to lead her a merry dance.
That time, I break her hip. The next time,
her tongue.
She doesn't need it: I have already stolen her words.
I am through the harder layers now, working my way to the soft centre.

—

Three years ago, they told us we heard the disease speaking. Now he is silent. He has almost devoured her, and he has a great deal to digest.

—

She is still breathing, but I am already beyond grief.
The feisty woman and her firework displays
have sputtered out.
There is only the glow of the heartwood's embers.
When people ask how I feel, I say
I am almost beyond caring.

—

He will draft her funeral service. He will play 'Over the Rainbow' for the girl with the little dog and the big dreams who got caught in a tornado. He will hope to go home with a new heart, a fresh brain. With courage.
Later, he will scatter her ashes like precious seeds, but she will not grow again.

—

As I tuck her feet into the wheelchair's stirrups, I pause to admire her ruby slippers.
I kneel to click their heels together, but she is not transported.

—

The carer's words are soft as a baby's blanket.
'Almost over now, David. I'll wait outside.'
I don't hear her leave, just the music starting over, faint as
breathing. A *Song of India's* rhythm like slippered feet on a
dancehall's floorboards.
Their song. Him, long since asleep in the Garden of
Remembrance. Her, dozing in her queen-sized cot.
As I hold her hand, she is as remote as history. As distant
as the jade-eyed girl in the Hammersmith Palais. Faraway as pea-soupers and ration cards, as black-outs
and litters of puppies in boxes under the stairs. Back
in a Battersea backyard, hiding licorice allsorts in her
knicker-legs from her brother's thieving fingers.
Sight, hearing, taste, smell. One by one, she
takes leave of her senses. All gone but touch. I
stroke a hand as dry as parchment, its words
indecipherable.
She holds onto her last breath, a little girl
clinging to the string of a balloon.
When she no longer has the weight to

tether it, it floats up and away. Gone.

"Sleep well, Mum,"
I whisper as I kiss her goodbye.

———

I slip away, leave him in the courtyard, shouting
at the apricot blossom for its hideous beauty, its
shameful timing. How can this be Spring?
He will act on, stumbling through the scenes as
best he can, improvising. In a few years, perhaps
someone will notice a shadow where no light could
cast one. As I creep onto the back of the stage,
maybe somebody in the audience will point.
'He's behind you!' they will shout.
    Maybe the first time, I'll let him remember his lines.
           But I will have the last laugh. **H**

Wanna

Dance?

by Edvige Giunta

Skinny, skinny legs, no period yet, and tiny mounds I check daily to see if they are ready for support. Three months away from my thirteenth birthday, I stand in the minuscule fitting room of a store on the Corso that sells good-quality lingerie. My mother draws the curtain to the side to peek inside and check which bra fits best, make sure it's roomy enough to last a few months. She's not about to waste money on a bra that fits snugly. We agree on a white embroidered padded bra, no underwire, size zero. And so adolescence begins, in Gela, the town on the Sicilian coast where my ancestors had settled generations earlier. It's March 1972. I can't wait to show Margherita my first bra. She already has one.

Margherita and I obsess over breasts. Size, shape, nipple, areola. We lock the door of my room and stand, braless, in jeans, facing the oval mirror above the cream-white dresser. Measuring tape at hand, we count fractions of centimeters and compare. I think hers are nicer. But my older sister and her best friend always ask me to show them my pretty breasts.

'Come on, *facci vedere*,' they say, looking up from their philosophy books. *Let's see.* I lift my t-shirt, snap the white bra, and two seconds later, with a coy smile, I pull my bra and t-shirt down.

'*Che belli!*' The high-school girls say and return to studying Marx.

I first met Margherita at the orphanage on Via Pascoli, a street of old people and quiet talk where centuries-old houses extended back into flourishing gardens. Margherita's aunt sat behind the railing of a Juliet balcony, a few feet above the ground, and watched people walk by. Tight-lipped and polite, Suor Lidia oversaw the orphanage. My grandfather helped her with the bookkeeping, which was why one day, when I was eight or nine, I walked through the door of the orphanage and met a dark-haired girl with spirited eyes.

Like many Sicilians, Margherita's parents were emigrants. People left Sicily all the time in search of work. They went to Northern Italy, Switzerland, France, Germany, even America. Margherita's parents had emigrated to Belgium, but left their daughter with her aunt so that she could attend school in Sicily. They planned to move back one day. They believed it would be easier for Margherita to have an Italian education.

One day the orphanage moved to a big, sad building surrounded by a sparsely cultivated, sickly garden. Whispers echoed through the dark, scantily furnished rooms. Margherita didn't sleep in one of the narrow beds in the large dormitory.

She had her own room, a small, narrow rectangle, a nun's cell devoid of the knick-knacks and posters that adorned mine. We'd sit on her bed and pretend to do homework. Then, we'd go to Suor Lidia to tell her we needed my mother's help with the homework. She'd nod lightly, smile stiffly at me, then utter a string of recommendations in the dialect of her hometown in the Sicilian interior. Sometimes I didn't understand her, and Margherita would later translate. We'd walk out of the gate, arm in arm, leaving behind the dreadful orphanage and her keeper.

In 1969, Margherita and I begin middle school. We sit together, in the first row. With scrawny legs and knobby knees, I am the nerdy girl who wears hand-me-downs from my older sister and cousin and helps Margherita with homework. She is easily bored, a little bird trapped in an austere life.

We'd sit on her bed and pretend to do homework. Then, we'd go to Suor Lidia to tell her we needed my mother's help with the homework

The cool girls in my grade, like Rina Morello and Rosa Di Dio, gossip about me in thick Sicilian dialect, as if I cannot understand them. I speak only Italian because my parents forbid me from speaking the dialect, which they consider low-class, though they use it between themselves and often when they speak to me and my siblings. I understand them as I understand my classmates' words of ridicule. They refer to me as '*'ssa babba*', '*scimunita*', '*ddrummisciuta*', and never fail to comment on my less-than-fashionable outfits: '*Ma comu si cumminau?*' I know I am not dumb, but I also know that my clothes deserve mockery. The girls who snicker at me wear miniskirts, fishnet stockings, and faux leather thigh-high boots. They wear bright red lipstick, dark blue or brown eyeshadow, eyeliner, mascara so thick that it leaves tiny lumps on their eyelashes. On a school trip to Siracusa, instead of the jeans and t-shirt of the other girls, I wear black patent leather shoes, white anklets, a sleeveless red-flowered cotton dress that belonged to my sister and hangs loose on my pre-adolescent body and, to top it all off, a twilled woolen checkered pink and gray jacket, another hand-me-down. This is a small victory since I've refused to wear the matching gray short-sleeve dress that prickles my skin.

In plain pants or skirts and sweaters, Margherita looks less pitifully childish and clownish than I do. Although she is not one of the cool kids, she's quick, savvy. She isn't the teacher's pet like I am, a studious, well-mannered daughter of teachers in a provincial town where name, class, and reputation mean everything. Our classmates talk to Margherita in dialect, and she answers in the tongue I am forbidden to speak.

Everything changes in the fall of 1972, when we start high school at the Liceo, where my older sister and parents had been students. We study Latin, Greek, Italian literature, philosophy, history. But family history and cultural heritage don't matter to me. What matters is the *passeggiata* – the ritual evening stroll on the Corso – secret motorcycle rides and dance parties, and the excitement of my body in tight jeans and a t-shirt, my new uniform. What holds my attention above all else is Margherita – and the boy we both want.

Marco, Marco, Marco: the kid everybody likes, the charming buffoon of the class. Even the teachers smile at his jokes. He is our first love, the boy who chooses me *and* Margherita, breaks up with one and, within weeks or days – even the same day – makes out with the other. For months I talk incessantly about Marco to Margherita before the triangle begins – or before I become aware of it.

One November day, Marco and I go to Margherita's to study for a school project. Marco sits in the middle, our three chairs so close in the nun cell that my leg and arm touch his. Oblivious of my best friend, I'm absorbed by Marco's handsome face, the deep-set green eyes, the full lips that remind me of Mick Jagger's – and the fact that I will walk home with him. On the way back, we take the dark back roads. Our hands brush against each other. I reach for his hand and our fingers entwine. I cannot wait to tell Margherita. Soon Marco will ask me to become his girlfriend. Oh yes, he will.

The dance parties are held at a sparsely furnished house on Via Pantelleria, a tiny street near the harbor owned by the uncle of a boy in our group. They start at five or six in the evening, and end early, because girls need to be home by eight. Nothing fancy: a record player, vinyl records –

mostly forty-five, but also a few LPs – with posters of Jimi Hendrix and Jimmy Page, and one of an adolescent boy and girl kissing, adorning walls in need of a new coat of paint. The room is lit by red and blue light bulbs we ambitiously call *luci psichedeliche*. When teachers or janitors are on strike and school is closed, parties start at ten in the morning and last until school closing time, when we head home and never mention to our families that there had been no school that day.

The declaration of love is scripted, bare: *Sei impegnata? Vuoi diventare la mia ragazza?* Are you taken?

The dance floor is the place for courtship and *dichiarazione d'amore* – how a boy asks a girl out, then moves on to the next girl if his first choice rejects him, as is often the case. The declaration of love is scripted, bare: *Sei impegnata? Vuoi diventare la mia ragazza?* Are you taken? Do you want to become my girlfriend? We collect up to ten 'declarations' in one evening – but never make such declarations to boys ourselves.

First kisses, hands groping beneath t-shirts, tongues snaking inside ears, hickeys we hide under carefully positioned scarves: this all happens at the house, *la casa*, as do break-ups, accompanied by tears, or dignified, sullen silence.

February 1973. Lucio Battisti's 'I giardini di marzo' plays. It's a favorite for slow dancing, next to Mick Jagger's sensual whispers in 'Angie' and the scandalous 'Je t'aime (moi non plus)' and 'La decadanse,' sung by Jane Birkin, a skinny blonde who launched the 'nude look', and her lover, French singer Serge Gainsbourg. Replete with heavy breathing, 'La decadanse' should be danced with the male embracing the female from behind – though we never dare. These hits that have reached the unglamorous rooms serving as teenagers' discos in provincial Sicilian towns are the songs I'm dying to dance to with Marco. Now Margherita dances with Marco. I dance with another boy. A few other couples move slowly, rhythmically, in small circles. A girl typically rests her hands on a boy's shoulders. Or her arms wrap around his neck, hands entwined, or one hand holds the wrist of the other and hangs loosely over the boy's upper back – depending on how much she likes that boy. Timid boys place their sweaty hands lightly on a girl's hips. The more daring boys encircle the waist and pull the girls towards them. I am focused on Battisti's song. With his husky voice, he is the songwriter of our generation. I adore his danceable rhythms and cryptic lyrics that hint at complicated passions and painful betrayals.

'La decadanse' should be danced with the male embracing the female from behind – though we never dare

My back is to Margherita and Marco. I hope that he'll ask me to dance next. Girls don't invite boys to slow dance. It's not done, unless a girl has the reputation of being 'easy'. Girls sit or lean against the wall until a boy approaches slowly.

'*Vuoi ballare?*' Wanna dance? He may ask. Or he may simply look in the girl's direction, slightly tilt his chin, and extend his hand. If a fast track plays, like Joe Tex's 'I Gotcha,' Stevie Wonder's 'Superstition', or Tina Turner's 'Nutbush City Limits', unaccompanied girls can join, uninvited, the circle of boys and girls who shake hips, arms, heads, hair. I wish I had long hair, like Margherita, instead of my boyish haircut.

I maneuver my body away from my grinning partner. His arms encircle my waist. His clasped hands descend towards my ass as he pushes his groin towards me. I squirm, and shift myself as far away as possible from the protuberance I feel through his tight, low-waisted, wide-legged pants. To put space between my body and my partner's requires all my concentration. He spins me around. That's when I see Marco and Margherita kiss. Their eyes are closed. I know you are supposed to keep your eyes closed when you kiss. Margherita has told me so. I've never kissed a boy. I want Marco to be my first.

Marco pulls Margherita towards him and rocks her gently. Her long, wavy brown hair cascades down her back, a soft mass that sways, alive, in rhythm with the music. My partner spins me around once again and for a few seconds I am spared the sight of my first betrayal.

My heart beats fast. I feel it everywhere, this pulse: neck, throat, stomach, legs. I am nauseous; I want to sit down, but I let my partner lead me, now oblivious to his advances. Margherita's face is flushed. She glances at me, then looks up at Marco and smiles.

When the song ends, I walk to the wicker loveseat. Marco and Margherita stand in the center of the room, eerie in the blue and red light. The next track begins. Someone walks toward me.

'*Balli?*'

I nod and follow him.

On the way home, we walk in silence, Margherita ahead of me, almost diagonally. I nurse the shock and sting of betrayal, but also feel the burden of our silence. The responsibility to end it, to decide the course of our relationship, falls upon me. So, I tell her that she is my best friend, that I won't let a boy, any boy, not even Marco, come between us. She says nothing.

When we get to my home, Margherita waves goodbye. *See you tomorrow in school.* I ring the doorbell. The ache in my throat and chest deeper now, I climb the five flights of stairs, rush to lock myself in the bathroom, sit on the toilet, and weep quietly. Afterwards, I walk into the kitchen, set the table, and answer my mother's questions about the *passeggiata*.

'*Chi c'era in piazza?*'

I recite a list of people I have supposedly seen near the main square, where she expects Margherita and I to have spent the evening, strolling up and down, under the watchful eyes of the town. Then I sit at the table with my mother and siblings. Afterwards, I help my mother clear the table, then enter the room I share with my older sister, the same room where Margherita and I have confided in each other our secrets, and plotted to evade the adults' control.

In my adolescent universe, the events of that evening hit hard, a lasting lesson on how all beliefs, expectations, loyalties can dissolve in one moment of a kiss. Margherita's turn to watch me kiss Marco would come a few months later. She, too, would hold on to our friendship, until it would be my turn again to watch, then hers again.

After that February dance party, Margherita and Marco start going out together, which means that they make out at dance parties, kid around in school. She blabbers about him all the time, as if sharing the details of their romance might assuage the hurt of the unnamed betrayal that settles between us.

> **She blabbers about him all the time, as if sharing the details of their romance might assuage the hurt of the unnamed betrayal that settles between us**

I stop talking about Marco, but I'm jealous. Secretly, terribly jealous. I tuck away the hurt and we even go out on double dates. Marco and I still flirt, harmlessly, since I am now dating Francesco.

I'm not crazy about Francesco, even though he's smart, popular, a grade ahead of me. I don't like his dark, thick, coarse, longish hair, and his stocky frame. His jeans are too loose, his t-shirts ill-fitting. How I admire the way Marco's jeans fit those long legs of his, the butt, round and firm. His biceps, wrapped by the sleeves of always-tight t-shirts, the toned muscles of his chest and belly that press against me when we dance. I love the tiny gap between his front teeth. I compare Francesco to Marco and find the former lacking. I don't like the way Francesco's wide-open mouth kisses. I don't like his thick, raspy tongue that moves too quickly inside my mouth, his hand that limply massages my breasts over my cotton t-shirt. Yet I welcome his attention and let him kiss and touch me – though I remain unresponsive. I feel a lazy curiosity, as if watching a movie with a tedious plot but with an occasional interesting scene.

> ## When he tightens his grip around my waist, I go limp. Bittersweet minty gum and tobacco lingers in my mouth

When Marco breaks up with Margherita, I dump Francesco. I tell Margherita I don't need a boyfriend, that it's more fun to go out with just her, our evenings no longer centered around boyfriends.

One evening, Marco unexpectedly kisses me, on the same dance floor where I had seen him and Margherita kiss three months earlier. His lips are delicious. His hot breath in my ear causes the most pleasurable tingling. He kisses my temples, my cheeks, my neck. His mouth makes its way back to mine. My greedy tongue responds to his. Heat rises in the back of my neck, my head. When he tightens his grip around my waist, I go limp. Bittersweet minty gum and tobacco linger in my mouth.

Nearby, Margherita pretends to be absorbed by whatever her dance partner is saying. Our eyes meet for a fraction of a second. Neither of us acknowledges the other. I hear her forced laugh, one I don't recognize. What I do recognize is the need to hide the hurt. Yet, I don't mind at all that she has seen us kiss.

When Margherita and I leave, I don't apologize. It's a cool night but we wear short sleeves because we're eager for summer. Faded Roy Roger's jeans, identical t-shirts – we even have identical blue Mary Jane-style flats. I walk with my head high. Margherita looks down. Her hair falls forward. It covers her cheeks. I know that her pain is caused by the pleasure that lingers in my body, the soreness of my lips from Marco's kisses. I had been in Margherita's shoes three months earlier. No guilt allowed.

When we arrive at my home, Margherita doesn't stop to chatter, to point out the evening's events deserving of giggles and gossip: who made up with whom, the boy who asked five girls to become his girlfriend and was turned down by all of them. She doesn't ask if I will meet her to walk to school together the next morning. She waves a tired goodbye and mumbles something.

'*Ciao*,' I say.

I remain outside for a few seconds. Her shape grows smaller. As I ring the doorbell, I think of the sad, solitary evening that awaits her.

'*Chi è?*' My mother's voice pulls me away from Margherita.

I hear the familiar click of the heavy wooden door, walk inside, close the door, lean against it. My lips feel swollen. I comb my hair with my fingers and shiver as I remember Marco's fingers through my short hair, how they pressed on my scalp, traced delicately the contours of my neck, moved down my back, slid under my t-shirt, made their way to my breasts. I press my hands against my cheeks. They feel hot. I take a deep breath and try to change my expression, to convey an innocence I don't feel.

I climb the five flights of stairs, two steps at a time, still flushed. A new feeling rises within me, like a distant, dull, persistent noise. It bothers me. I don't want anything to ruin this night. Guilt, glee, revenge, shame, pity: they fuse together as I swallow the bittersweet taste of another betrayal. I push the feeling away. I only want to get to bed and fall asleep, lulled by the evening's memories and the anticipation of tomorrow.

The following day, I don't talk to Margherita about the previous night. I decide that my actions do not constitute a betrayal, but a rebalancing. Margherita knew I liked Marco first. She should never have gone out with him. Marco was mine. Margherita had been an intrusion. She doesn't say anything, not even to repeat what I had said three months earlier, when I had declared my devotion to her – it had been nothing but a reprieve.

Instead, Margherita hastens to offer advice in romantic matters. She warns me to turn off the light when Marco and I retreat to the other room in the house, which has a bed with a worn mattress.

'*Spegni la luce*,' she urges me. With the light on, he will look at me, especially my breasts. To be seen by a boy isn't a good thing, Margherita explains. Boys don't think much of girls who allow their private parts to be seen.

'But his eyes are closed,' I protest, wondering why being touched is OK but being seen is not.

'That's what you think.'

She assures me that his eyes are wide open and checking me out, because that's what boys do. And I should keep my own eyes closed.

I promise to turn the light off and keep my eyes closed.

Boys only respect girls who are 'difficili, the opposite of 'facili'. I know I am never to tell Marco I love him. I am not that stupid

And it isn't good, she says, to let him touch me wherever he wants, even if I like it. There's a protocol regulating male-female intimacy which I need to learn. I know nothing about where and when it's OK to be touched. To be touched. Because girls are supposed to be touched, not touch. Touch is the prerogative of boys. I have broken these rules from the start, by entwining my fingers with Marco's when we walked home from Margherita's. I feel embarrassed about my lack of experience and misguided audacity.

'Don't let him pull down your pants, or touch you down *there*,' she says. I don't tell her this warning comes too late.

Margherita is adamant: '*Non fare la facile.*' Boys only respect girls who are '*difficili*', the opposite of '*facili*'. I know I am never to tell Marco I love him. I am not that stupid.

'Pretend that you don't care. *Se no ti lascia.*' Marco will surely break up with me unless I play hard to get, Margherita insists. And since he's going around telling people I am 'easy' – he has told Margherita so himself – I should break up with him first, to save face.

Less than two weeks after we start dating, I break up with Marco, and he gets back together with Margherita. At the end of June, my birthday party is held at the notorious house. I watch Margherita dance with Marco while I flirt with several boys. Then she leaves, earlier than I do. Because it's my birthday, my mother has extended my curfew. Margherita is barely out of the door when Marco saunters towards me.

'Wanna dance?'

After a year of almost daily dance parties, I finish the school year with Ds in all subjects, except English and Geography, in which I manage to get Cs. Marco must go to summer school. Margherita must repeat the year. Her parents, however, won't allow it. They had left her behind in Italy to study, not to waste time and drive her aunt crazy. They want her in Belgium with them.

Margherita is barely out of the door when Marco saunters towards me. 'Wanna dance?'

We beg her parents to let her stay. Even my mother and my grandfather put in a good word.

'School is the most important thing,' my mother says with teacherly authority – but Margherita's parents cross their arms and tell Margherita to pack her bags.

In mid-July, the train on which Margherita travels to Belgium stops in Catania where I am spending the month at my aunt's. I ask my uncle to take me to meet her.

Margherita and I cling to each other, promise to write, to stay friends forever. Right before the train departs, she confesses that she has been with Marco one more time while I was away.

'The only reason he stays with you is because he wants to make out,' she whispers in my ear.

I cry harder.

We hug tight, sobbing. She boards the train and leans out of the window. I reach out to hold her hand. The train leaves and I wave until it becomes a tiny spot, then disappears. In the car on the way home, I cry hard until my uncle tells me to cut it out, that nobody has died. I sniffle and weep silently. While I miss my best friend, I am relieved that my rival is gone.

My parents were indignant about my grades and my teachers were embarrassed for not doing a better job with their colleagues' daughter. Yet if I had failed, I would not have been sent out to work. I would have been back in school, after studying all summer under the guidance of teachers who knew my parents and would have refused any payment. But I did not think of how fortunate I was, how my social class was shaping my life so differently from my friend's. Factory work awaited Margherita. She was fifteen.

I wrote to Margherita daily, then weekly, then monthly. A year later, she returned to Sicily for the summer, but our lives had become too different. When she visited me, she wore a bright red mini-dress and high heels. Her hair was pulled back. She wore make-up. We took pictures on the verandah of my house, on the spiral iron staircase that led to the rooftop terrace. If she had seen Marco, she didn't tell me.

Margherita got married a couple of years later, at the age of eighteen. I attended her wedding in a somnolent town in the Sicilian interior. Framed by her bridalwear, she looked so much older. Youth and rebellion had been drained out of her.

By the time I finished high school and moved to Catania to attend college, we had lost touch. Sometimes, my grandfather would bring me news of my old friend. She was pregnant. She had given birth to a girl. I knew my grandfather talked about me to Margherita's aunt, who reported back to Margherita, who would ask about me when she visited her aunt.

Marco and I continued, on and off, for another year or so. After an all-too-familiar back-and-forth between me and yet another girl, he dumped me during a two-minute phone call. We were both fifteen.

In the later years of high school, I saw Marco almost every day. Although I pretended not to care, my heart skipped a beat every time I saw him or heard his voice in the corridors of the Liceo. He was as popular as ever, but he was getting good grades now. His classroom was next to mine, and I would linger outside to catch a glimpse of him. Occasionally, we would end up at the same party and at times danced together. He would hold me tight, like old times. I felt the pleasure of physical closeness and the simultaneous sorrow of how ephemeral this was. I believed we would eventually get back together again, that his relationship with his girlfriend of the last two years was temporary. I was so sure he would come back to me. But he never did. When I watched him get serious with yet another girlfriend, I realized he wasn't going to break up with this one.

I believed we would eventually get back together again, that his relationship with his girlfriend of the last two years was temporary

Margherita's departure had changed nothing for me and the boy over whom two best friends had fought, mostly silently, without mercy. I had no one to tell of my new realization, my fresh sorrow, no one who would understand. I had lost both my first loves.

Who loved me best?

Margherita, whom I forgave but also betrayed?

Marco, untouched by the turmoil he had caused in the two girls who loved each other as well as him, with whom I would never talk about any of it?

And whom did I love best? **H**

OUT NOW

boilerhouse.press

LITTLE BOY
by John Smith

ISBN 9781913861063

"Little Boy is an extraordinary novel,
audacious and poignant
and superbly well-written. It
imagines the unimaginable,
finds innocence in awfulness.
This is what the literary novel
is capable of, but so rarely pulls off..."

– Andrew Cowan

Editor's Choice, *The Bookseller*

BOILER

HOUSE

PRESS